A guide to
Sterkfontein
the Cradle of
Humankind

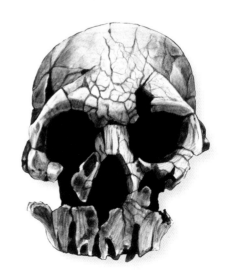

Prof. Lee R. Berger
Brett Hilton-Barber

Struik Publishers
(A division of New Holland Publishing (South Africa) (Pty) Ltd)
Cornelis Struik House
80 McKenzie Street
Cape Town
8001

New Holland Publishing is a member of the Johnnic Publishing Group.
www.struik.co.za

Log on to our photographic website
www.imagesofafrica.co.za for an African experience.

First published in 2006
1 2 3 4 5 6 7 8 9 10
Copyright © in text 2006: Brett Hilton-Barber & Lee R. Berger
Copyright © in illustrations 2006: Walter Voight (pages 1(top), 3, 50, 67–82),
other illustrations © Struik Publishers, 2006
Copyright © in published edition 2006: Struik Publishers

Managing editor: Lynda Ingham-Brown
Editor: Joanna Ward
Design concept: Janice Evans
Designer: Patricia Lynch-Blom
Cover Design: Robin Cox
Illustrators: David du Plessis & Walter Voight
Indexer: Cora Ovens
Proofreader: Tessa Kennedy
Reproduction by Hirt and Carter Cape (Pty) Ltd
Printed and bound by
Craft Print International Ltd

ISBN 1 77007 257 8

Picture credits
Richard du Toit: p. 37; Gallo Pictures: p. 9; Gauteng Government: p. 15, p. 29,
p. 30, p. 32, p. 35, p. 39, p. 43, p. 44, p. 45, p. 47 (bottom), p. 57;
Brett Hilton-Barber: p. 47 (top); Ian Johnson: p. 4, p. 11, p. 13, p. 17, p. 19, p. 28, p. 34; Images
of Africa p. 7, p. 25, p. 46; Lee Berger: p. 40 (top); Museum Africa: p. 22 (bottom), p. 23,
p. 26; NASA: p. 16; National Geographic: front cover;
South African Library: p. 22 (top); Trevor Sampson/Business Day: p. 40 (bottom).

CONTENTS

CHAPTER ONE

THE CRADLE OF HUMANKIND

The 47 000 hectare Cradle of Humankind is a unique location blessed with a greater wealth of the prehistory of humankind than almost any other place on Earth. Officially called the Sterkfontein, Swartkrans, Kromdraai and Environs World Heritage Site, the Cradle contains more than 12 major fossil sites and dozens of minor ones that present us with an intriguing mixture of mystery and revelation about much of our ancient past.

The Cradle of Humankind lies in the Witwatersrand Basin on the edge of the divide between the highveld grasslands and the more vegetated bushveld in the South African province of Gauteng. It is a summer rainfall area where the higher lying reaches are rolling grasslands while the well-watered valleys have thick riverine bush thinning into mixed woodlands on the slopes.

Beneath the 2,6-billion-year-old dolomitic hills found in the Cradle of Humankind lies a series of extensive underground caverns. These geological time capsules have preserved the fossil remnants of tens of thousands of extinct animals, as well as the bones and cultural remains of our own ancestors, the hominins.

Included in the Cradle of Humankind is the world-famous Sterkfontein Cave, which has become synonymous with the South African search for human origins. It is located in the dolomitic bedrock underlying the region. This bedrock was once an ancient sea bed and the valley contains some of the world's oldest undistorted rocks, dating back to between 2,6 and 2,8 billion years. That is just over half the age of the Earth itself!

The dolomites are the sedimentary remains of an ocean floor that hosted some of the earliest forms of life on Earth – prehistoric blue-green algae. These can still be seen in the rocks today in the form of fossilized stromatolites.

Through the ages, the area now designated the Cradle of Humankind has undergone a number of changes. Giant inland seas have come and gone, meteorites have struck near it and dinosaurs have roamed across its surface. The climate has varied considerably, but for the past 3 million years or so, during what scientists call the Plio-Pleistocene (the period when much of human evolution occurred), there has been less variation. During the early stage of the Plio-Pleistocene the Cradle of Humankind enjoyed a subtropical environment. It became much drier as a result of global cooling, yet it has always been conducive to hominin occupation because of the availability of water and shelter, and the varied animal and plant life.

HOMININ VERSUS HOMINID

Humans and their ancestors have generally been referred to as hominids in the literature of the recent past. Of late, however, a new, scientifically more appropriate term has come into play, namely 'hominin', which will be used in this book.

In 1758 botanist Carolus Linnaeus (or Carl von Linné) developed a binomial classification system that uniquely identified different animals and plants. This system is still used today, albeit in a modified form.

In the Linnaean system of classification, organisms with similar morphological characteristics were grouped together. Thus, humans are classified as Hominidae

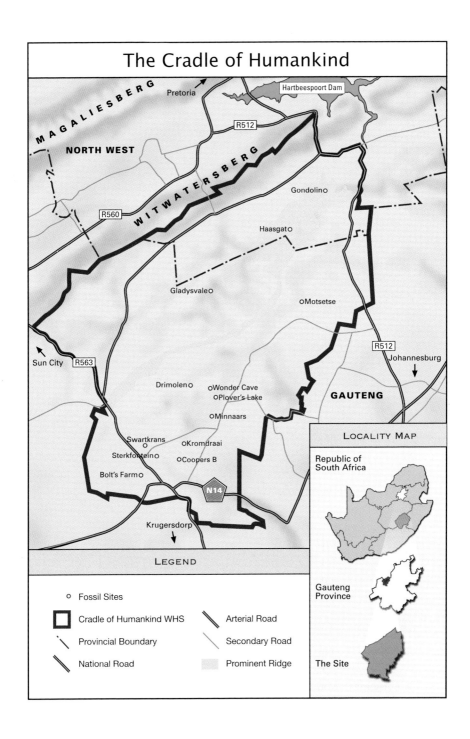

The Cradle of Humankind

MAGALIESBERG

NORTH WEST

WITWATERSBERG

Pretoria

Hartbeespoort Dam

R512

Gondolin○

Haasgat○

R560

Gladysvale○

○Motsetse

Sun City

R563

R512

Johannesburg

Drimolen○   ○Wonder Cave
             ○Plover's Lake

GAUTENG

○Minnaars

Swartkrans
○
Sterkfontein○   ○Kromdraai
             ○Coopers B

Bolt's Farm○

N14

Krugersdorp

LOCALITY MAP

Republic of
South Africa

Gauteng
Province

The Site

LEGEND

○	Fossil Sites		
☐	Cradle of Humankind WHS		Arterial Road
	Provincial Boundary		Secondary Road
	National Road		Prominent Ridge

because of certain characteristics that differentiate us from the other primates, for example bipedalism (the ability to walk on two legs). The Linnaean classification system also makes provision for superfamilies and the superfamily Hominoidea (hominoids) includes all the living apes. This is the starting point of the present debate on classification.

The traditional view has been to recognize three families of hominoid: the Hylobatidae, the Hominidae and the Pongidae. The Hylobatidae include the so-called lesser apes of Asia, the gibbons and the siamangs. The Hominidae include living humans and closely related fossil apes, such as the australopithecenes, that possess certain characteristics, for example bipedalism, reduced canine size and increased cranial capacity. The Pongidae include the remaining African apes and the orang-utan, whose 'apeness' is recognized in the fact that it is a large-bodied, tail-less, quadrupedal, arboreal primate.

Recent genetic research suggests that humans are much more closely related to two other members of the family Pongidae, the common chimpanzee and the bonobo, than either of these species is to the gorilla. We share almost 98 per cent of our genes with chimps, which indicates that humans share a recent common ape ancestor with the chimpanzees. Divergence times between the two groups suggest that the chimpanzee/human split occurred between 5 and 7 million years ago, while the chimpanzee/gorilla split took place about 7 to 9 million years ago.

Linnaeus, the father of classification.

The African apes are more closely related to one another than any of them are to the orang-utan. In turn, humans, chimps, gorillas and orang-utans are more closely related to one another than they are to the gibbons and siamangs. In recognition of these genetic relationships, some scientists argue that we must overhaul the present morphologically based classification system and replace it with one that is more representative of our true evolutionary relationships as evinced by our genes.

This is where the term 'hominin' comes into use. Under this proposed classification model, Hominoidea would be a primate superfamily, as has always been the case.

Orang-utans, gorillas, chimps and humans would fall under this hominoid umbrella in the family Hominidae. In recognition of their genetic divergence some 11 to 13 million years ago, the orang-utans would be placed in the subfamily Ponginae and the African apes, along with humans, would all be lumped together in the subfamily Homininae. The bipedal apes, namely living humans and all their fossil ancestors, would fall into the tribe Hominini (thus hominin).

As to the debate on whether to use the term 'hominin' or 'hominid', the growing pervasiveness of genetics in every aspect of our modern lives means that the term hominin will probably win out in the long run. It has many advantages in its precision and in its recognition of a biological reality that moves beyond physical morphology.

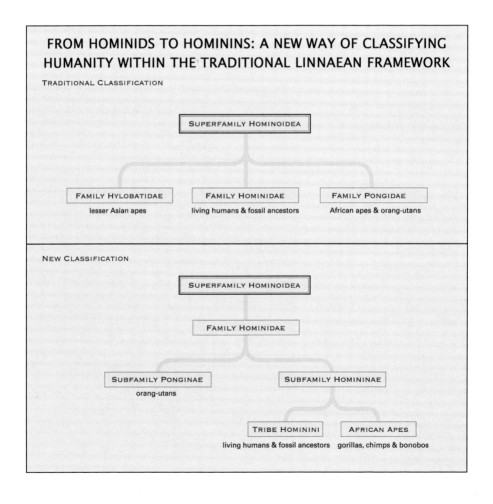

FROM HOMINIDS TO HOMININS: A NEW WAY OF CLASSIFYING HUMANITY WITHIN THE TRADITIONAL LINNAEAN FRAMEWORK

TRADITIONAL CLASSIFICATION

SUPERFAMILY HOMINOIDEA

FAMILY HYLOBATIDAE
lesser Asian apes

FAMILY HOMINIDAE
living humans & fossil ancestors

FAMILY PONGIDAE
African apes & orang-utans

NEW CLASSIFICATION

SUPERFAMILY HOMINOIDEA

FAMILY HOMINIDAE

SUBFAMILY PONGINAE
orang-utans

SUBFAMILY HOMININAE

TRIBE HOMININI
living humans & fossil ancestors

AFRICAN APES
gorillas, chimps & bonobos

STERKFONTEIN – UNLOCKING THE MYSTERIES OF THE PAST

It is a commonly accepted scientific assumption that we are the latest product of an evolutionary chain that split from the ancestral apes somewhere around 5 to 7 million years ago. There is incontrovertible fossil evidence that this split occurred somewhere in Africa, which is often referred to as the Cradle of Humankind. At least 13 different hominin species that evolved since the split have been identified, and discoveries of their remains have been concentrated in two main areas – East Africa and South Africa.

Chimps share almost 98 per cent of our genetic make-up.

While the finds in East Africa have been scattered through several countries, mainly Tanzania, Kenya and Ethiopia, the key to understanding human origins from a South African perspective is located mainly in the Sterkfontein area. This small piece of Earth has, remarkably, yielded over 35 per cent of the world's early hominin fossils.

The Sterkfontein site is the world's longest running archaeological excavation, having been dug continuously for the past three decades, and excavated intermittently during the three previous decades. Excavations have been undertaken mainly by scientists associated with the University of the Witwatersrand in Johannesburg and the Transvaal Museum in Pretoria.

Five or possibly six different hominin species have been found at the various sites in the Cradle of Humankind. In addition, three major tool cultures and a wide range of plant and other animal fossils have been found that provide a framework for the interpretation of human evolution.

What makes the Cradle of Humankind such a tremendous repository of ancient fossil treasure? The answer is a complex one. One important factor is the geological personality, or coincidence, of the area, which is favourable for the preservation of fossils. These vital clues to our past have withstood millions of years of the vicissitudes of environmental change.

A CAVE IS FORMED

Generally, caves in the Cradle of Humankind have followed six stages of cave formation:

Stage 1: A cavern forms through the dissolution of dolomite in what is known as the phreatic zone, the zone beneath the water table. Its original shape is usually determined by faults or planes of weakness in the rock.

Stage 2: The water table drops, usually because of the natural erosion, or cutting, of a nearby valley and the cave becomes filled with air. Stalactites and stalagmites now begin to form in the cave as surface water continues to percolate through the dolomite.

Stage 3: Avens, or shafts, start forming and gradually begin to approach the surface.

Stage 4: Avens break through to the surface. A talus cone may begin to form beneath the opening, filled with dirt, organic debris and bones of animals derived from the surface. If this cone becomes calcified by lime-bearing water dripping from the ceiling, it is cemented into what we term 'cave breccia'.

Stage 5: The cave is almost completely filled with cave breccia and the entrances begin to expand as a result of erosion.

Stage 6: During this final stage erosion or mining has de-roofed the cave entirely and the bone-bearing breccia is exposed.

Stage 1

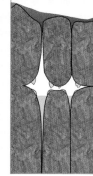

Stage 2

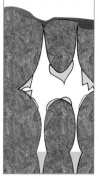

Stage 3

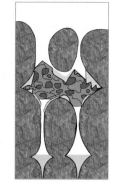

Stage 4

Stage 5

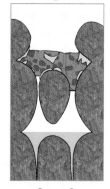

Stage 6

Sterkfontein valley.

Over time, dolomites erode and create pockets within themselves. Calcium carbonate, or limestone, the main component of the dolomitic bedrock, precipitates in these extensive pockets. When lime-rich solutions infiltrate the sand or bones on cave floors a form of concrete called breccia is formed. The breccia facilitates the long-term, stable and safe preservation of the remains of animals, and of ape-men.

While this has ensured that the quality of fossils from the Sterkfontein area is very good, the topsy-turvy stratigraphy of cave infills has made the actual dating of fossils a difficult and often controversial task.

The fossils themselves are extraordinary – not only the individual pieces, but the sheer volume of fossil fragments that has emerged from the various sites. More than 1 000 hominin fossil fragments, several hundred thousand animal fossils, 300 fragments of fossil wood and over

9 000 stone tools form a vast, multi-dimensional and continually expanding scientific jigsaw puzzle. These finds provide a compelling picture of the last 3,5 million years of South African prehistory.

Although several pieces of the puzzle are missing, and may never be found, there is growing evidence that modern humans may well have evolved in the southern part of Africa.

In brief, the puzzle that has been put together so far tells the following story: between 2 and 3 million years ago, a hominin with a blend of ape and human characteristics occupied the Gauteng highveld, seeking shelter in the riverine forests and foraging for food in the broken woodland. This ape-man, known by the scientific appellation of *Australopithecus africanus*, may well have been the ancestor of our own genus, *Homo*. Standing approximately 1,3 metres tall, with a brain about the size of a grapefruit, *A. africanus* lived in small social groupings, eking out a living from a subtropical landscape dominated by predators such as the false sabre-tooth cat *Dinofelis*, and populated with other now extinct creatures like hunting hyenas, giant leaf-eating monkeys and small primitive baboons.

The consequences of far-reaching climatic change between 2 and 3 million years ago created evolutionary pressure on the ape-men living in the Cradle of Humankind.

Excavations at Sterkfontein bear witness to an intriguing phenomenon, the possibility of a speciation window, that occurred between 2,5 and 2 million years ago when it appears that the morphology of one species began taking on the characteristics that would eventually lead to a separate species. Around this time, a certain population of *africanus* may have started to take on characteristics associated with the robust ape-man (a flatter-faced, larger-toothed australopithecine), while another population may have begun to resemble the earliest members of our own genus, *Homo*. Regardless, just after the emergence of the genus *Homo*, *africanus* apparently disappeared from the fossil record. Intriguingly, however, the early *Homo* species and the robust ape-man appear to have co-existed for hundreds of thousands of years, each grappling with rudimentary tool technology and occupying different ecological niches.

It seems that the robust ape-men could make use of bone tools – there is evidence that they used these at the sites of Swartkrans and Drimolen – while it appears that early *Homo* was responsible for the manufacture of stone tools, of which thousands have been found in the Cradle of Humankind, the earliest dating back to around 2 million years ago. But even these ideas may change in the light of new discoveries. There is emerging evidence from sites like Coopers, for instance, that many of the early stone tools may in fact have been made by the robust ape-men, and not by early *Homo* as had previously been thought.

THE MAKING OF A FOSSIL

The word 'fossil' is derived from the Latin *fossilis*, 'something dug up'. Fossils are the preserved remains of, or image of the remains of, a once living organism such as an animal or a plant. Even the traces left by a once living organism, such as footprints or trackways, are considered fossils.

Typically, fossils are recorded in sedimentary rocks that have been laid down by the actions of water. Fossilization is the process whereby an organism is transformed into a fossil. It usually involves the impregnation of pores and holes in the remains of the organism with minerals in solution. Minerals like calcium carbonate and silica are some of the more common fossilization agents, preserving bone for millions of years.

In other situations, water seeping through rocks may dissolve away the remains of an organism, leaving a cast of the original form. This cast is itself a 'trace' fossil, but it may be filled by other minerals transported by groundwater to create a replica of the original. Hard tissues such as bone or shell have a greater chance of surviving the fossilization process than soft parts like muscle, fat and hair.

In the Cradle of Humankind, most fossils are preserved either as casts or as permeated and replaced bones, but almost every other type of fossilization has occurred here. The most common mineral found in the fossilization process of this area is calcium carbonate that has precipitated from the surrounding dolomitic bedrock.

No fixed time of burial is required for the remains of an organism to be declared a fossil, but there is general consensus that some level of mineral replacement needs to have taken place.

Precipitating limestone in Wonder Cave.

The early *Homo* species, most commonly known as *Homo habilis*, were larger brained than both the robust and gracile australopithecines and were also more opportunistic – their varied diet meant that they developed superior hunting and scavenging skills, whereas *Australopithecus robustus*, which had a largely vegetarian palate, did not develop these skills. By 1,5 million years ago there was a noticeable change in stone tool technology that may indicate that *Homo erectus* was beginning to replace *habilis*.

At Swartkrans, a short distance from the Sterkfontein caves, there is even evidence that *Homo erectus* began to tame fire approximately 1–1,5 million years ago. It is not clear if this was captured fire or manufactured fire, but most scientists believe that this may be the first evidence of an ability to 'steal' fire from natural bush fires caused by lightning, and transport the flames into caves for warmth and protection.

Over time, *Homo* populations flexed their mental and social superiority, slowly coming to dominate the harsh and competitive environment of the African bushveld and eventually, around 1,5 million years ago, migrating northwards out of Africa and occupying habitable environments in Europe and Asia.

Around 1 million years ago, the robusts had followed the earlier ape-men into extinction, unable to survive in a world where the available niches were increasingly being filled by *Homo*. The story of *Homo*'s dominance and the inability of the robusts to evolve outside their specialist habitats can be found in the artefacts and bones of the Cradle of Humankind. In many ways, it is the story of our success as a species.

There is convincing evidence that the *Homo erectus* populations that remained in Africa evolved into an archaic form of *Homo sapiens* (our own genetic classification) between 800 000 and 200 000 years ago. Although the fossil record is sparse in this regard, it would appear that archaic *H. sapiens* was the first species to transform communication into recognizable language and to take on the trappings of contemporary human behaviour. Remains of archaic *H. sapiens* are to be found in the Cradle of Humankind, although the best evidence comes from the Western Cape coastline and the central Free State.

These pre-modern humans laid the foundation for the origin of our own species between 200 000 and 100 000 years ago. There is strong circumstantial evidence that this transition took place in southern Africa.

CHAPTER TWO

THE LIVING LANDSCAPE

The Cradle of Humankind World Heritage Site is a geological wonder. The area lies on the northern edge of the Witwatersand Basin, which has some of the richest gold ore deposits in the world while huge stores of platinum lie to the west. The ancient granites that are found in the Cradle of Humankind are almost three-quarters as old as the Earth itself. They protect a network of subterranean caverns formed over millions of years in the softer dolomites that preserve traces of the planet's oldest life forms as well as some of humanity's earliest ancestors. These mysterious underground caves are believed to extend over several kilometres. They have not yet been fully explored and at least one intrepid soul has lost his life in an attempt to map these underground caverns, many of which lie below the water table. Sterkfontein and Wonder caves (below) are the most accessible and beautiful of these magnificent caves.

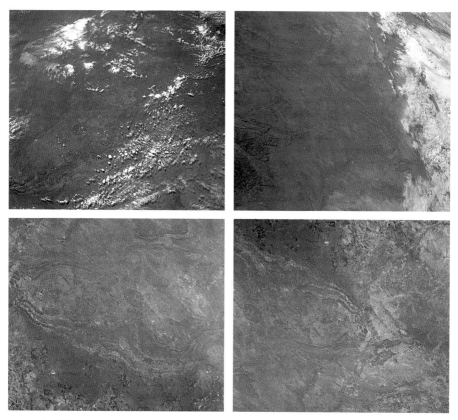

The Witwatersrand as seen from space, and taken from *(top left)* the space shuttle *Discovery* with an Aero-Linhof large-format camera, *(top right)* the space shuttle *Atlantis* with a 70 mm hand-held Hasselblad camera, and *(bottom left and right)* from the space shuttle *Challenger* with a 70 mm hand-held Hasselblad camera.

THE WITWATERSRAND BASIN

Three billion years ago the Cradle of Humankind was part of a large inland sea that stretched as far as the equator. This huge basin, which covered what is now southern Gauteng and the northern Free State, lay over a relatively stable part of the Earth's crust, the Kaapvaal Craton.

Surrounding this sea was a range of very high granite domes. Over time these mountains eroded, depositing their sediments in the relatively shallow waters of a continental shelf and low-lying coastal plains. As this erosion process continued, pebbles, sand and mud were washed into the deeper parts of the lake, eventually creating a 7,5 km-deep layer of primal rubble on the floor of the basin.

CAVE-FORMING DOLOMITES

The geological feature of most significance in terms of the preservation of early human origins is the Worldkarst, or cave-forming, dolomites that occur within the protected area of the Cradle of Humankind. This at least 1 220 m-thick layer of rock, formed at the bottom of the ancient sea beds 2,5 billion years ago, is recognizable from the way it juts out of the grassland and hilltops.

Tilted slightly northwards, the dolomites are generally inhospitable to larger trees as they do not support topsoil very well. It is only where caves have undercut an area of hard dolomite, or where streams and rivers have gouged their way into the rock and formed narrow floodplains, that larger plants can gain a foothold.

One of the ways in which scientists have identified areas in the dolomites where there may be caves is to look for the occurrence of lime-loving trees such as the Wild Olive *Olea capensis* and the White Stinkwood *Celtis africana*. Often, their presence marks the top of an underground cavity into which their roots grow.

Unfortunately, many of the magnificent stinkwoods that must have grown in the hidden valleys of the Cradle of Humankind were felled at the beginning of the 20th century to use as fuel for lime furnaces, and so only their stumps remain as clues to where potentially fossil-rich caves might be.

White stinkwoods and wild olive trees are lime-loving and their presence is often an indication of an underground cavity.

Two different dolomite formations exist in the Cradle of Humankind. The dolomites in the south of the area, around Sterkfontein and the traditional fossil sites, are part of the older (2,6 to 2,8 billion years old) Monte Cristo formation, which reaches as far as Drimolen and the Rhino & Lion Nature Reserve. These rocks are flatter and more block-like than those in the northeast near the sites of Gladysvale, Motsetse and Gondolin, which are from the younger Eccles formation (2,3 to 2,5 billion years old).

From the surface one would never guess that within the dolomites winds a honeycomb-like network of underground caves that stretches for many kilometres. A large number of these passages are under the water table and are thus not accessible without scuba gear.

One can often identify the presence of a cave beneath the surface by the trees growing in the mouth or by the presence of a sinkhole, which is caused when the ground collapses into an underlying space.

Caving opportunities abound in the area, but some routes are definitely not for the claustrophobic. For the less intrepid, the Wonder Cave is an excellent opportunity to see unmined flowstone formations and fossils in the making. The Sterkfontein underground tour offers a close-up look at a more extensive system and an underground lake, but one that has been damaged by mining. Remember that one needs permission to enter caves, and that it is illegal to collect any cave formations. Moreover, it can be extremely dangerous to venture into the caves on one's own as many of them are still occupied by predators such as hyenas and leopards. These animals – along with porcupines – are the most common bone-collecting mammals in the area today, exhibiting the same behaviour as their ancestors did millions of years ago.

One of the noticeable features of the geology of the Cradle of Humankind is an orange-coloured 'topping' on some of the rocks, known as giant chert. This feature is particularly visible from the Kromdraai or Hartebeeshoek roads. There is some debate as to how old this chert is. The conventional wisdom has been that these rocks are the eroded remnants of a dinosaur-aged Cretaceous landscape 65–75 million years old. This has prompted some intrepid palaeontologists to look for dinosaur remains in these sediments. However, recent research suggests that the giant chert may be closer in age to the dolomites, which would make these rocks 2,5 billion years old. But the actual age of these rocks remains uncertain and awaits further research.

Also scattered throughout the Cradle of Humankind are small pockets of other types of rock and minerals. A sharp-eyed amateur geologist might find outcroppings of lead, copper and umber. The many mining pits that are scattered throughout the area attest to the mineral potential that early explorers recognized in the area.

CHAPTER THREE

IN SEARCH OF HUMAN ORIGINS

Beneath the grasslands and dolomitic outcrops of the Cradle of Humankind lies an extensive series of underground caverns that have preserved clues of our most ancient past. For the better part of the last century, the Sterkfontein caves and surrounding fossil sites have been the focus of the southern African search for human origins.

Since Robert Broom's discovery of an adult ape-man specimen at Sterkfontein in the mid-1930s, research in the Cradle of Humankind has shaped much of our thinking about the relationship between the australopithecines and our own genus, *Homo*. Subsequent fossil finds have proved beyond doubt that humanity originated in Africa, and indeed evidence suggests that the emergence of our own species may well have occurred in South Africa.

The first recorded discovery of the Sterkfontein caves, initially known as the Kromdraai caves because of the name of the adjoining farm, was by a group of students from Marist Brothers College in Johannesburg, who explored the caves in 1895 and found fossils embedded in the limestone caverns. However, the man usually credited with finding Sterkfontein is Guglielmo Martinaglia, a lime-worker who blasted the surface openings of the caves in 1896.

Soon thereafter a Mr David Draper from the Geological Society of South Africa explored the caves and reported back to the Society that he had found them most interesting from a geological point of view, and that there was much to be discovered there. Draper was an intrepid explorer and self-taught geologist who pioneered the geological exploration of the Witwatersrand and was respected internationally for his diamond exploration in Brazil. Today, in his honour, the Geological Society of South Africa bestows the Draper medal for outstanding services to geology.

Lime was in great demand by the gold-mining companies, which had been established in the 1880s, for gold processing and by the building industry for the manufacture of cement. It soon became apparent that there was a conflict of interest between geologists and the prospectors and miners who dynamited the lime out of the rocks. Draper's timely intervention in 1897 prevented the caves from being completely destroyed. He successfully persuaded the company that owned the mineral rights to preserve the main cave because of its impressive stalactite and stalagmite formations and its pristine underground lake. Although the main Sterkfontein cavern was thus preserved, blasting operations continued in the immediate vicinity.

At a meeting of the Geological Society of South Africa on 13 September 1897, a Mr ME Frames reported the presence of 'animal remains found in the Kromdraai Caves in the dolomite near Krugersdorp. Amongst these are those of the horse species, antelopes, monkeys, porcupines, rats, bats etc., and the presence of the first two in the cave would lead us to infer that they had been dragged there by beasts of prey'.

(BROOM & SCHEPERS, 1946:46)

Surprisingly, although the palaeontological significance of the Sterkfontein area was recognized in the late 19th century, it was not for another three-and-a-half decades that any serious scientific work was undertaken. During this time many specimens were probably destroyed by the lime-mining operations. As the famous fossil finder Robert Broom later wrote, 'It is sad to think that for nearly 40 years no scientist ever paid the slightest attention to these caves; and probably some dozens of skulls of ape-men and all the bones of their skeletons were burnt in lime kilns' (Broom & Schepers, 1946:46).

The caves did, however, attract the attention of tourists, particularly after the discovery of the Taung skull in 1924, when the search for fossils caught the South African public's imagination. Many fossil specimens were found around Sterkfontein by amateur souvenir hunters, and indeed many were offered for sale at the little tearoom next to the main cave. The owner at the time, a Mr RM Cooper (after whom the Coopers site is named), had even written a rough guide to the fossil site in which he used the slogan 'Come to Sterkfontein and buy your guano, and find the missing link', which, as Broom wryly observed, was a 'strangely prophetic remark'.

An artist's impression of the Taung skull discovered in 1924.

THE DISCOVERY OF THE TAUNG CHILD

The discovery in 1924 of the Taung child, some 480 kilometres away from the Cradle of Humankind, had a profound effect on the way the world would eventually come to view Africa. The tiny skull, not much bigger than the size of a grapefruit, was blasted out of the lime deposits at Buxton, just outside the village of Taung in the Northern Cape.

The skull found its way into the hands of Professor Raymond Dart, an Australian who had just taken up the post of Head of Anatomy at Wits University. Dart was immediately struck by the ape-like head and human dentition of the little skull, which suggested it was of a previously unknown species located biologically somewhere between ape and human. Dart worked feverishly once he had the skull in his hands, and the speed with which he made his analysis was a contributing factor to the international controversy that the little skull caused.

Just four months after the discovery, Dart published his findings in the scientific journal *Nature*, announcing that he had found the intermediate creature between ape and man. The international response was overwhelmingly negative. This can be attributed to the bias of the time, which held that the origins of humanity lay either in Europe or Asia, to the fact that Dart had been unseemingly hasty in his pronouncements and also because his whole theory was based on a single specimen of a juvenile nature.

Prof. Dart and the Taung skull.

It was to take over 20 years before the pendulum of international opinion swung back in Dart's favour, and *Australopithecus africanus* was finally declared to be a part of the human family tree. This recognition was due largely to the efforts of the Scottish-born Dr Robert Broom, an enthusiastic supporter of Dart's, who came to his defence and found an adult version of the Taung child while working at Sterkfontein. Broom believed that the discovery of another ape-man fossil, particularly an adult specimen, would silence Dart's critics, and at the age of 70, when many others were retiring, this became his mission in life.

From left to right: Dart, Broom, Breuil, and Van Riet Lowe.

CHAPTER FOUR

THE CRADLE OF HUMANKIND AND ITS FOSSIL SITES

Taung flagged South Africa's importance in the search for human origins. But Raymond Dart's announcement of the discovery of an intermediate species between ape and human was greeted with as much scepticism as support. Further corroboration was needed to prove that the Taung skull was not just a freak of nature but part of a consistent pattern of human evolution located in Africa. Dart's pursuit of fossils in the Cradle of Humankind not only led to the discovery of new hominin species, but laid the foundation for world recognition that the Gauteng fossil fields provided some of the key pieces in the puzzle of human ancestry. Although his early successes were confined to Sterkfontein and Kromdraai, further scientific research has yielded important fossil evidence at several other sites in what has subsequently been declared the Cradle of Humankind.

THE SEARCH MOVES TO STERKFONTEIN

The Taung discovery showed that fossils were most likely to be found where there were extensive lime deposits and it was for this reason that Broom, soon after he had engineered an appointment to a post at the Transvaal Museum in Pretoria in 1934, started concentrating his search on the area of Sterkfontein on the West Rand.

He visited several sites in the area. His hopes were raised and subsequently dashed when a museum colleague informed him that he had come across an ancient-looking human jaw embedded in the wall of a cave called Gladysvale, north of Sterkfontein. When Broom investigated he found no trace of the jaw, concluding that it must have been prised loose by souvenir hunters.

However, his luck would change. In July 1936 two of Dart's students, GWH Schepers and H le Riche, visited Sterkfontein and noted the excellent fossil-finding conditions and extensive lime-quarrying taking place there. They alerted Dart and then Broom to the site's potential by showing them a fossilized baboon skull found there.

Broom made his first trip to Sterkfontein on 9 August 1936. To his delight he discovered that the chief quarryman at Sterkfontein and caretaker of the caves, GW Barlow, had worked at Taung and had been present when the Taung skull was found. Barlow told Broom that he was certain similar skulls had previously been found at Sterkfontein and promised to keep a sharp lookout for such specimens in the future.

Broom was lucky. Three days later, on 12 August, he visited Sterkfontein again and Barlow gave him 'three nice little fossil baboon skulls and much of the skull of a large sabre-toothed tiger' (Broom & Schepers, 1946:46). His interest was piqued, and he began searching the area with more vigour. On 17 August, only his third visit to Sterkfontein, Broom was handed the blasted-out natural brain cast of an anthropoid by Barlow, who asked 'Is this what you're after?' Broom replied, 'That's what I'm after' (Broom & Schepers, 1946:46). These words marked the beginning of a new chapter in the study of human origins.

Barlow showed Broom where he'd found the skull and the Scottish doctor soon unearthed a rather battered and incomplete skull, jawbone and teeth of what appeared to be an adult australopithecine. However, as Broom studied his find he came to believe that the teeth and other elements of his specimen differed markedly from those of the Taung child, so much so that in his view it was a different species altogether. This was a characteristic peculiarity for which Broom would become famous: the naming of a new species or genus with almost every fossil discovery.

Eventually he settled on a name for his new find, *Plesianthropus transvaalensis* (Near Man from the Transvaal), assigning the fossils not only to a new species, but to a new genus as well. The search for human origins was beginning to get complicated.

...

Broom's excitement at his new find was dampened by the reaction of the international scientific community, which, as a result of discoveries in China in 1931, still favoured Asia as the birthplace of humankind and was not very interested in finds of 'apes' from Africa. His determination remaining intact despite international scepticism, Broom redoubled his efforts and continued his search in the foothills around Sterkfontein.

Sterkfontein

Sterkfontein has become synonymous with the South African search for human origins. It is also the world's longest running archaeological dig, having been excavated continuously since 1969. Since its discovery in 1896, Sterkfontein has yielded approximately 500 hominin fossil fragments, approximately 9 000 stone tools and thousands of animal and plant fossils that have given us a unique insight into human evolution over the past 3 million years. At least three hominin species are represented at Sterkfontein – these are Australopithecus africanus, Paranthropus robustus and an early version of Homo.

Sterkfontein's most famous find is probably Mrs Ples (Sts 5), the 2,5 million-year-old australopithecine fossil that confirmed the theories of Professor Raymond Dart that humankind evolved in Africa. Other notable finds from Sterkfontein are Stw 53 (believed to be 1,5 to 2 million years old), a fossil that may be a transition species between the australopithecines

and early Homo, and the more recently discovered Little Foot (Stw 573). Although Little Foot has not yet been fully described, it appears to be the oldest australopithecine yet found in South Africa. There remains some controversy over its age, which is between 2,6 and 3,3 million years old.

Sterkfontein, which is administered by the University of the Witwatersrand, is the most accessible site in the Cradle of Humankind. It also has evidence of some of the oldest life on Earth in the form of stromatolites, which were colonies of algae that existed approximately 2,5 billion years ago.

Inside Sterkfontein.

THE ECCENTRIC GENIUS ROBERT BROOM

Robert Broom with one of the many fossils he discovered.

Robert Broom is one of the most colourful and controversial characters in the history of South African science. The tall, eccentric Scottish-born doctor is best known for his discovery of Mrs Ples, the fossil remains of an adult ape-man, at Sterkfontein in 1947. Broom was 81 years old when he found Mrs Ples. Dart recalled that 'Although [Broom] was a great evolutionist, he was nevertheless a deeply religious man. He even believed spirits led him to his discoveries' (SABC:54).

Broom was born into a poor and very religious family of Plymouth Brethren in Scotland in 1866. He had little formal education and developed his interest in science working as an unpaid lab assistant in the Chemistry Department at the University of Glasgow. He managed to enrol as a medical student and graduated in 1889 with honours in midwifery. He travelled extensively before settling in South Africa in 1898, where he practised medicine to support his true love of palaeontology. He was fortunate to have developed a direct line of communication with the then prime minister, General Jan Smuts. This relationship was to prove very valuable given the number of enemies Broom cultivated during his long career. Smuts had a soft spot for Broom: 'Long years ago I knew him as a medical practitioner in a small South African dorp where medicine kept the family pot boiling while his heart dwelt far away among the reptiles of the Mesozoic age . . .' (Broom & Schepers, 1946:3).

In 1903 Broom was appointed professor of geology and zoology at Victoria College, Stellenbosch, and during the next seven years, with a free railway pass obtained through the South African Museum, he visited every known fossil site in South Africa, and discovered many new ones. Broom spent a lot of his free time exploring the Karoo and, from the fossils he found there, he developed a basic framework demonstrating the evolution of mammals from reptiles.

In 1910 the Railways rescinded his free pass when the then minister of railways, JN Sauer, proclaimed that the study and collection of fossils was a matter of no interest to the country. It was partly the attitude of the authorities that impelled him, during a lecture tour to New York in 1913, to sell a number of fossils he had borrowed from the South African Museum in Cape Town to the American Museum of Natural History, prompting outrage among his scientific colleagues.

Broom subsequently furthered his medical studies in Great Britain before resettling in South Africa in 1916. This was the bleakest part of his life, as he felt like an outcast from the scientific community. He practised medicine in the small town of Douglas on the fringes of the Karoo, serving as the mayor of the town in 1920. During that year he was admitted as a Fellow to the Royal Society of South Africa, which restored his spirits somewhat.

Broom had begun to shift his interest to early hominids after hearing of the discovery of Boskop Man, the first human fossil skull found in South Africa. He wrote a paper on it in 1918, labelling it *Homo capensis*.

His interest in anthropology was overshadowed by his palaeontological interests. When the Broken Hill skull (now known as Kabwe) was found in 1921 by T Zwigelaar in what is today Zambia, Broom became certain that the origins of humanity must have lain in Africa. Thus, when Taung was discovered, he was very excited. Dart recalls how Broom arrived in his office at Wits in his characteristic black suit and announced: ' "I'm Broom. I know your old chiefs . . . I've come to see your little skull." So he came over to the table on which the cardboard box holding the little skull then rested and, dropping on his knees, held it in his hands "in adoration", as he remarked, of "our ancestor" '(SABC:58).

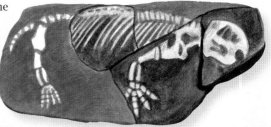

An illustration depicting the *Diictodon feliceps* fossil discovered by Broom.

Broom's charisma enabled him to bounce back from the setback of being ostracized by the scientific community and the enormous energy he put into his work earned him the respect of the then prime minister, Jan Smuts, who ensured that a palaeontology post was created for him at the Transvaal Museum in Pretoria in 1934.

During the late thirties and forties Broom concentrated his search for hominins in the Sterkfontein valley. His work was controversial because of his liberal use of dynamite to extract fossils. However, this approach did produce results that made him world famous by bringing to light Mrs Ples and the Kromdraai Ape-man.

Broom died in 1951, driven to the end to complete his monograph on the Swartkrans hominins. He completed the final corrections on 6 April 1951 and wrote in his journal 'Now that's finished . . . and so am I'. He passed away that evening.

Kromdraai

Kromdraai is the site of the first discovery of a robust ape-man in the world. Schoolboy Gert Terreblanche found a jaw and several teeth at the site, which drew the attention of Robert Broom in 1938. The Kromdraai ape-man (TM 1517) has been classified as Paranthropus robustus. Some five other hominin fossils have been discovered at Kromdraai, as well as hundreds of animal fossils and a variety of early Stone Age tools. Among the interesting mammal fossils found at Kromdraai include those of an extinct giant wildebeest, an extinct springbok, eland and kudu.

THE FIRST 'ROBUST' APE-MAN

On 8 June 1938, the quarryman Barlow contacted Broom and said that he had found something special: it appeared to be part of an australopithecine palate and a first molar. Broom was puzzled because the matrix in which the fossil was set was different from the rock around Sterkfontein. It was also far more robust than the type of specimen he was looking for. After being questioned, Barlow revealed that the fossil had not been found at Sterkfontein, but by a schoolboy, Gert Terreblanche, on the neighbouring farm of Kromdraai, some 1,5 kilometres away.

Broom immediately set out for the farm, only to find that Gert was at school. He persuaded the boy's sister to take him to the hillside where the fossils had been found. After fossicking in the dust, Broom found a fossil tooth. This find was enough to persuade him to hurry straight to the young Terreblanche's school.

At the school Broom explained his mission to the principal and Gert was duly summoned to his office. The boy produced four fossil teeth from his pocket, which Broom persuaded him to surrender for a shilling apiece. Under the Scottish doctor's gentle interrogation he admitted to having prised the teeth out of what appeared to be a jawbone embedded in the rocks.

Broom wanted to return to the site immediately, but the principal pointed out that there was still another hour-and-a-half of school time, and suggested that Broom lecture the children on the importance of fossils and how caves were formed.

Broom, dressed as always in the formal black suit and starched wing collar that gave him the appearance of grave authority, had no difficulty enthralling his

The Kromdraai fossil, TM 1517, discovered in 1938.

young audience with his tales of searching for fossils. Once the class was over, Gert took Broom to the fossil site, where Broom found the skull from which the teeth had been taken. Although the skull had been smashed by the schoolboy's crude dental extraction, there were sufficient fragments to allow for reconstruction. This material, plus a further tooth that Gert had stashed away, was handed over in exchange for five chocolate bars.

The whole area was subsequently searched thoroughly and the topsoil carefully sieved by members of the Transvaal Museum staff. The result was the discovery of major portions of the skull, which could be adequately reconstructed – but it varied considerably from earlier finds. It was altogether more massive, particularly the jaw, which supported unusually large molars. Broom, after recovering and cleaning the specimen, pronounced the find a new species of ape-man, *Paranthropus robustus* (a robust creature akin to man).

The discovery of the Kromdraai fossil (labelled TM 1517) marked a turning point in world opinion, as the significance of the fossils coming out of South Africa could no longer be ignored. After visiting Sterkfontein and studying the australopithecine specimens Broom had recovered, two leading American scientists, William K Gregory and

THE EXCAVATORS: UNSUNG HEROES

Over the years most of the actual digging of the Sterkfontein site has been conducted by a dedicated group of men who work five days a week, 48 weeks a year to extract fossils from the hard breccias found at the site. Several of the men have been working at the site since its opening in 1966 and have made an invaluable but often unrecognized contribution to the furthering of our understanding of human origins. But the public's recognition of their efforts is growing. With the discovery in 1997 of Little Foot, the oldest australopithecine yet found in South Africa, the two men who actually found the specimen deep in the underground cave were given recognition for the remarkable achievement. For Stephen Motsumi and Nkwane Molefe, finding the matching tibial fragments was as difficult as finding the proverbial needle in a haystack.

As times have changed in South Africa, so has the level of recognition of the critical role played by the mostly black field technicians, the people at the front line of palaeoanthropological research in the Cradle of Humankind.

Excavators Joseph Sekowe *(foreground)* and Lucas Mothobi at Coopers.

Milo Hellman, concluded that these were 'in both a structural and a genetic sense the conservative cousins of the contemporary human branch' (Gregory, 1939).

Buoyed by this support, Broom began further excavations at Kromdraai in 1941, but his mood gradually turned to disappointment as the sterile breccia revealed few fossils of significance, with the exception of a juvenile australopithecine jaw. Broom closed down the site and, during the years of the Second World War, focused on writing an overview of the significance of the ape-men. He published his findings in 1946, shortly before he turned 80. His conclusions confirmed Dart's original hypothesis that the australopithecines had walked upright and that, although they had small brains and ape-like faces, their teeth were human-like. Broom's analysis led him to believe that they had the ability to use tools and that, based on the animals he found with them, they probably lived in open country.

After fossicking in the dust, Broom found a fossil tooth.

In 1947 Broom and his new assistant, JT Robinson, renewed the excavations at Sterkfontein, using dynamite to blast away the hard breccia in which they hoped to find hominin fossils. Their heavy-handed techniques raised the ire of other scientists, who argued, with some justification, that explosives destroyed the context of the fossils, making it impossible to date them. Broom's response was that the rock-hard nature of the sediments left him little choice but to employ such drastic measures, and that the caves held little context in any case.

The National Monuments Council disagreed and banned Broom from further work at Sterkfontein unless he was accompanied by a field geologist. Broom, who had served as a professor of geology and zoology at Victoria College in Stellenbosch, was outraged and appealed to Prime Minister Smuts, among others, for support. The Commission backed down and a defiant Broom continued blasting at Sterkfontein. Within a few days his efforts paid off.

MRS PLES

On 18 April 1947, Broom and Robinson blasted an almost complete australopithecine skull out of the Sterkfontein Cave wall. The blast had split the skull into two fragments, but had not damaged the specimen irreparably. The skull was clearly that of an adult version of the Taung child, and Broom believed it to have been that of a middle-aged female. Broom christened the find *Plesianthropus africanus*, which the media soon shortened to 'Mrs Ples'. Broom was later to write: 'I have seen many interesting sights in my long life but this was the most thrilling in my experience' (Terry, 1974).

The remarkable string of finds would continue. On 1 August that same year, Broom and Robinson blasted out a slab of breccia that contained the partial thigh bone, several

THE IMPORTANCE OF MRS PLES

Why is Mrs Ples one of the most important characters in South Africa's fossil family? The 2,5-million-year-old ape-man fossil provided the evidence that Raymond Dart needed to prove that the Taung child was an intermediate genus between human and ape, and that humanity's roots were in fact African.

Mrs Ples, coined from the scientific appellation *Plesianthropus transvaalensis*, was later reclassified as *Australopithecus africanus* once the skull had been studied in greater detail by other scientists.

In early 2002, after renewed studies of Mrs Ples, palaeoanthropologist Francis Thackeray concluded that the skull was that of a male. However, it is unlikely that Mrs Ples will be renamed Mr Ples.

vertebrae and more or less intact pelvis of an australopithecine. These remains, labelled Sts 14, proved that australopithecines were indeed upright walkers, or bipeds. Although the pelvic bones were smaller than those of modern humans they were not wholly dissimilar in shape and form, whereas they were very markedly different from those of apes. By the end of 1947, Broom had amassed further specimens, including a lower jaw with teeth.

Mrs Ples, or Sts 5 (her museum catalogue number), represented a vital turning point in the broader acceptance of South African australopithecines as hominins. The discovery of an adult cranium negated criticism that the Taung child was nothing more than a juvenile ape. Sts 5 demonstrated without doubt that had the Taung child grown up, it would not have developed into a chimpanzee or gorilla.

The discovery of Mrs Ples captured the imagination of the international scientific community and South African fossil hunters began receiving more support. In 1947 the British Association offered Broom 'its congratulations on the brilliant success of his recent exploration of the Sterkfontein site. His new discoveries amplify and confirm in a remarkable way his interpretation of the earlier finds and also provide a vindication of the general view put forward by Professor Raymond Dart in his report of the first Australopithecus skull found in 1924' (Berger & Hilton-Barber, 2000).

> 'Since one of the two ape-men seemed clearly to be on the line
> of human descent and the other to have specialised away from
> that line, Broom's finds compelled scholars to realise that not all
> early hominids were direct ancestors of modern mankind. Some
> were on side branches. This meant that at an earlier period
> the two species, so closely related to each other, must have
> branched off from a common ancestor. The pattern of hominid
> evolution was not like a linear Chain of Being after all. It was
> like a bush of branches, only one of which made the grade to the
> later stages of human evolution, while the other branches were
> doomed to ultimate extinction.'
>
> (PHILLIP TOBIAS, 1994)

In 1948 Broom switched his attention to the nearby site of Swartkrans, just across the valley from Sterkfontein, where he and Robinson found several more hominins. In 1950 Broom and Robinson produced a preliminary description of Sts 14, but it was not until 1972 that Robinson, who became renowned for his authoritative studies of australopithecine teeth, published a detailed description of the find. Robinson continued working on the block of breccia from which the Sts 14 pelvis came, recovering a number of previously unknown vertebrae and ribs, adding greatly to our understanding of the locomotion of those particular hominins.

After the highlights of the forties, the fifties were in many ways a depressing time for palaeoanthropology. Few exciting fossils were found and funding was consequently harder to come by. The rise to power of the National Party in 1948, with its fundamentalist and separatist views, effectively ended any chance of government support scientists might have enjoyed. The ousted prime minister, Jan Smuts, had displayed a keen personal interest in human evolution, to the point of encouraging his son to study the geology of Stone Age sites. This passion was unfortunately not shared by his successors. Indeed, the new prime minister, DF Malan, was philosophically wary of the unbiblical notion that humankind had evolved from an ape-like ancestor, and the notion of common ancestry did not suit the emergent apartheid ideology.

Despite the negative attitude of the government of the time and the lack of funding, the fifties witnessed a breakthrough in the understanding of the complicated cave systems in the dolomites. The relationship between fossils and the caves in which they were found had always troubled scientists because of the lack of a generally accepted cohesive interpretive framework. This problem was solved by the efforts of a young geologist who had been invited by Robinson to conduct a detailed study of the geology of the Swartkrans site shortly before it was closed down in 1951.

Swartkrans

Swartkrans is a cave close to Sterkfontein that is most famous for being the site of the earliest known evidence of the controlled use of fire. Bob Brain of the Transvaal Museum discovered 20 ancient hearths in the cave dating back to approximately 1 million years ago. He analysed some 270 burnt bones found at the cave and concluded that they were deliberately burnt. Evidence of the domesticated use of fire elsewhere in the world has been dated to approximately half a million years ago. Other finds at Swartkrans include the fossils of a robust australopithecine (Paranthropus crassidens) discovered by Robert Broom and John Robinson in 1948 and the jaw of an early Homo that Robinson discovered in 1949. These two finds showed that the gracile and robust ape-man species co-existed at the same time around 1,5 million years ago. One of the most complete skulls of a robust ape-man (SK48) was found at Swartkrans in 1950 and has been dated to between 1,5 to 2 million years old). Interesting animal fossils found at Swartkrans include remains of the extinct giant buffalo (Pelorovis antiquus) that had horns that stretched 3 metres from tip to tip.

Charles Kimberlin ('Bob') Brain's work at Swartkrans and other caves was eventually published as his PhD in 1958, titled *The Ape-Man Bearing Cave Deposits of the Transvaal*. During this time, working with Revil Mason and Alun Hughes, Brain found the first evidence that early hominins in the Cradle had been stone-tool makers.

The other seminal work to come out of the 1950s was Revil Mason's *Prehistory of the Transvaal*, published in 1962, in which Mason introduced a mathematical approach to working out the complicated relationships between South African Stone Age cultures.

THE ART OF STUDYING THE GRAVE

Brain succeeded Broom and Robinson when he was appointed palae-ontologist at the Transvaal Museum in 1965. One of his first actions was to revive the Swartkrans dig, which had been dormant for 12 years. Brain's thorough analysis of the Swartkrans fossils led him to the conclusion that most of the bones were accumulated in the caves by scavengers and predators that used the caves as feeding and breeding lairs.

This raised an interesting philosophical question that challenged the theory argued by Dart in the late forties, namely that the fossil bones were the result of bloodthirsty fighting between killer apes who bludgeoned each other to death with weapons made of bone. This idea, formally labelled the osteodontokeratic culture (bone, tooth and horn), gained such popularity that Stanley Kubrik used it in his opening sequence of the film *2001: A Space Odyssey*.

Through a series of compelling and elegantly simple comparative studies of modern accumulating agents such as hyenas, leopards and porcupines, Brain proved conclusively that the fossils in the cave sites were not collected by early hominins, but by animals. Our ancient heritage was not bathed in the blood of violence between our ancestors – we were the hunted, not the hunters. In making such a convincing case, Brain almost single-handedly founded a new field of science, now known as the science of taphonomy, or study of the grave.

Bob Brain undertook a detailed study of leopard behaviour to understand how fossils ended up in caves.

Brain's 1965 re-opening of Swartkrans began a 25-year excavation that would not only make Swartkrans the second-richest site for hominin fossils (Sterkfontein being the first) but also set the standard by which all future excavations of South African caves would be judged.

At the same time that Brain was embarking on his revolutionary studies, another significant development occurred. Sterkfontein was saved from obscurity and possible destruction in the early sixties when the land on which the caves stand was donated by the Stegman family to the University of the Witwatersrand. Phillip Tobias was a prime motivator in rescuing the

site and renewing the excavations, which began again in 1966, the same year that the little Robert Broom Museum was opened at the caves.

For years there was almost no reward for the hard work of removing tons of breccia from Sterkfontein, a labour-intensive exercise that occurred under the supervision of a heavy-set Welshman, Alun Hughes. Ten years of hard work yielded only 50 or so assorted hominin fragments, which were difficult to interpret because most weren't found *in situ*.

Hughes spent two or three days a week at the site supervising the ten excavators and preparators employed by the University, patiently cataloguing the few finds that emerged from the rubble. A grid system was established, consisting of steel girders, wire and nylon fishing line. The excavation was conducted in spits that measured 900 mm by 300 mm.

It was not until 1976 that the first significant hominin was recovered from a context that could be clearly identified. Stw 53 was the first evidence of a new type of hominin at Sterkfontein, one that was more advanced than the australopithecines, and thus difficult to place in a taxonomic category. Initially classified as *Homo habilis* because of its less protruding face, head shape, tooth-wear pattern and larger brain capacity, it was later argued that it might be *H. ergaster* or even an advanced australopithecine; the jury is still out, however.

In 1978 geologist Tim Partridge came up with a geological model for interpreting Sterkfontein's complicated stratigraphy. He introduced the concept of 'members' for the deposits, labelling them in sequence from oldest to youngest, Member 1 being the oldest deposit, dating back possibly beyond the 3-million-year mark, while Member 6 is the youngest at a mere 100 000 to 200 000 years old. The richest deposit for hominin material so far has been Member 4, which contained most of the *africanus* specimens recovered from Sterkfontein to date.

By the late 1980s excavations at Sterkfontein were penetrating down into a partially decalcified cavity that has often been referred to as the 'swallow hole', owing to its abundance of australopithecine fossils. Almost

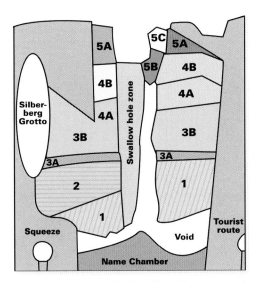

Sterkfontein members (1 is the oldest, 5 is most recent).

THE TAMING OF FIRE

Swartkrans has produced the oldest evidence yet discovered of the domestic use of fire. During his excavations, Bob Brain discovered 20 spits or hearths in a section of the cave, the oldest being over a million years old.

Of the 350 000 or so pieces of bone found at Swartkrans, 270 appear to have been deliberately burnt. In a series of comparative studies, Bob Brain showed that the burnt bone remains were consistent with the results produced when bones were burnt in experimental campfires made from White Stinkwood (*Celtis africana*), one of the most common trees of the area. Controlled fires appear to have occurred repeatedly in the gulley as it was filling up, indicating long-term use by hominins.

Brain has noted that it is 'likely that fire management was based on fire gathered from natural conflagrations caused by lightning strikes, with the ability to make fire at will only coming much later. But even this kind of management was a technological advance of immense significance, giving early hominids a measure of protection from predators, badly needed when sheltering in caves at night' (Brain [ii], 1998).

all of the specimens from this cavity, which measures approximately 8 x 10 metres, are relatively well preserved, with very little crushing. The 'swallow hole' is the deep excavated area in the centre of the site (see diagram on page 36).

By 1989, Hughes and Tobias had catalogued some 550 hominin specimens from Sterkfontein alone. The two men had been collecting fossils almost continually since 1966. Across the valley at Swartkrans, Brain was also making headway. In a quarter of a century of his custodianship of the site, 350 000 fossil pieces had been recovered. Brain's approach to site excavation set the standards for subsequent digs. It is a little known fact that almost every site in the Cradle of Humankind today is dug based on methods devised and implemented by Bob Brain at Swartkrans.

In the course of this work, Brain would also make dramatic discoveries about our origins. He would find evidence of, and subsequently prove, the earliest controlled use of fire on the planet, more than 1 million years ago. Brain insists that the story told by Swartkrans was that 'far from being mighty hunters, the early hominids formed an insignificant part of the fauna of the time and they were certainly subservient to carnivores such as leopards and sabre-tooth cats. They had been the hunted, rather than the hunters' (Brain [i], 1981).

Brain also demonstrated the existence of a bone tool culture, possibly used by the robust australopithecines. The wear patterns on sharpened bones he found at Swartkrans and other sites led him to believe that stones were not the only form of early tool, and that the use of tools by early hominins was more widespread than had previously been imagined. By 1990 the Cradle of Humankind projects undertaken by the Transvaal Museum and Wits University were at a crossroads. Tobias was approaching retirement, Brain was completing his Swartkrans study – and funds were drying up.

GLADYSVALE AND DRIMOLEN: A NEW ERA

Then came Gladysvale. The site that had originally been explored by Broom, and then Tobias, yielded the first new hominin material in 1991, making Gladysvale the first new hominin site discovered in South Africa in 44 years. A Wits University team led by Lee Berger found an australopithecine tooth, the first of a dozen hominin remains and thousands of other fossils that would be unearthed. In terms of quantity of fossil-bearing breccia, Gladysvale is the largest fossil deposit in the Cradle of Humankind.

Shortly afterwards, geologist André Keyser found the remains of robust australopithecines at the nearby site of Drimolen. These two discoveries generated a new surge of interest in palaeoanthropology, and highlighted the importance of South Africa as a locus for the search for human origins.

Berger and Johannesburg art dealer Mark Read, whose family owns the Plover's Lake site in the Cradle of Humankind, discussed the need to raise funds to exploit the new finds and came up with the idea of creating a non-profit organization along the lines of the Leakey Foundation, which had raised considerable sums of money for scientific research in East Africa.

Gladysvale

Gladysvale is one of the new generation sites in the Cradle of Humankind. In 1991 an excavation under Prof. Lee Berger discovered several hominin fossils making it the first

new hominin-bearing site in South Africa in over 40 years. Approximately 38 000 animal fossils have been recovered from Gladysvale, including the remains of a large, extinct, wolf-like animal. Gladys-vale, which is in the John Nash Nature Reserve, has one of the most extensive cave sequences in the Cradle of Humankind, with sediments dating from approximately 3 million years to 250 years ago.

A fossil antelope jaw discovered at Gladysvale.

Drimolen

Drimolen is one of the most exciting of the 'new generation' fossil sites in the Cradle of Humankind, and the third richest in the area in terms of fossil material. Discovered only in 1992 by Dr André Keyser of the Council for Geoscience, it has yielded a rich harvest of hominin fossils. Some 82 hominin specimens from Drimolen have so far been catalogued. Most of these are robust ape-man species and there is an as yet unidentified form of Homo. The site is believed to be between 2,5 and 1,6 million years old. Among the more unusual hominin remains that have been found are the jaw of a Homo child aged about 11 and the fossilized teeth of an eight-month-old robust australopithecine. A variety of plant and animal fossils have been found including those of ancient hyenas and baboons.

The cranio-dental remains of a *Paranthropus* female found at Drimolen.

The Gladysvale australopithecine teeth.

They attracted the interest of Anglo-American chairman Gavin Relly, who helped launch the Palaeo-Anthropology Scientific Trust (PAST) in 1994 and put together a team of South African businessmen and -women to ensure continued funding for the important work being carried out. PAST very quickly succeeded in raising funding for a number of headline-making projects.

LITTLE FOOT

The South African palaeoanthropological renaissance started to gain momentum after the first democratic elections in South Africa in 1994. The end of the academic boycott and lifting of international sanctions against South Africa allowed it to re-enter the scientific mainstream. PAST's fund-raising efforts, combined with re-awakened international interest in South Africa, gave the science a boost – and created an ideal environment for the emergence of Little Foot.

The story of Little Foot is characterized by a remarkable chain of coincidences. The little australopithecine skeleton might well never have seen the light of day had it not been for the persistence of Ron Clarke, the field officer at Sterkfontein, appointed after Alun Hughes' death in 1993. In 1994 Clarke was going through some bags of previously

Nkwane Molefe, Ron Clarke and Stephen Motsumi with the Little Foot foot bones.

collected material when he found a number of hominin foot bones that had been overlooked. These 12 little bones displayed a mixture of ape and human characteristics, showing that their owner had been comfortable both walking on the ground and climbing in trees. The find was named Stw 573. Three years later Clarke was rummaging through other fossils stored in the Wits strongroom when he found a foot bone (intermediate cuneiform) that fitted that of Stw 573. Clarke found several other bones that pieced together the foot and ankle bones of Stw 573 and showed that it was more ape-like than human. The bags from which the bones were found convinced him that the rest of the skeleton must still be in the Sterkfontein caves, most likely in an area known as the Silberberg Grotto.

An illustration of part of the buried skull belonging to Little Foot.

At the end of June 1997 he gave a cast of the distal fragment of the right tibia to two of the fossil preparators at Sterkfontein, Stephen Motsumi and Nkwane Molefe, and asked them to search the cave surface of the Grotto. 'The task I had set them was like looking for a needle in a haystack, as the grotto is an enormous, deep, dark cavern with breccia exposed on the walls, floor and ceiling. After two days of searching with the aid of hand-held lamps, they found it on 3 July 1997 near the bottom of the Member 2 talus slope at the western end of the grotto. The fit was perfect, despite the bone having been blasted apart by limeworkers 65 or more years previously' (Clarke, 1998).

For the next year the three men chiselled away at the hard rock, trying to expose the rest of the skeleton. To their consternation, they found that an ancient collapse of the cave wall had separated the top part of the skeleton from the lower part. In September 1998 they found part of the arm bones and a portion of the skull. The skeleton is still embedded in the rock, so a detailed analysis of what it might be still has to be carried out. Clarke says initial indications are that it is an australopithecine, but that it seems to have unusual characteristics compared to the other specimens of that genus found at Sterkfontein.

Initially Partridge, Clarke and others dated Little Foot at 3,3 million years old. However, a revised dating model published in 2002 by Berger and others suggests that it may be a million years younger. Nonetheless, Little Foot is the most complete australopithecine early hominin yet discovered in South Africa.

'Alun Hughes used to tell me of a recurrent dream that he had of his breaking into a cavern and finding a complete skeleton of an Australopithecus lying there. I am pleased, through strange circumstances, it has been my good fortune to realize Alun's dream and bring to fruition the expectations of Phillip Tobias that an archaic form of Australopithecus would be recovered from the lowest levels of Sterkfontein.'

(RON CLARKE)

By 1998 the South African palaeoanthropological revival was in full swing. A major international scientific convention, the Dual Congress, was held that year. It showcased the South African view of human origins and demonstrated that a unique evolutionary pattern was unfolding south of the Limpopo, one that was different from the East African model.

PAST has become the largest palaeoanthropological fundraising body in the world, sponsoring some 14 excavations in southern Africa, many of these located within the Cradle of Humankind.

COOPERS

What Little Foot had demonstrated was that established fossil sites still had as much potential for surprise as new sites. This was also to prove the case with Coopers, a site situated midway between Kromdraai and Sterkfontein. Coopers had looked promising way back in the 1930s, when a researcher named Middleton-Shaw had found a single hominin tooth there. At the time there was some controversy surrounding the find, fuelled by accusations that the tooth had actually been taken from Sterkfontein by one of the students. Brain examined Coopers during the 1950s and came to the conclusion that it could not conclusively be considered a hominin site.

While the original Coopers tooth went missing during the 1960s or 70s from the Wits Dental School, where it was housed, another tooth from Coopers cropped up at the Transvaal Museum in 1994. There, Martin Pickford came across a single tooth in a collection of boxes marked 'Coopers'. In a paper written by Lee Berger, Pickford and Francis Thackeray, it was suggested that the tooth appeared to belong to *Homo*, but because it was found out of context this could not be stated beyond doubt.

Berger decided to revisit Coopers and began a test excavation at a part of the site known as Coopers A. He sent one of his students, Christine Steininger, to the Transvaal Museum to study the fossilized fauna from Brain's excavation. To her surprise she found a badly crushed hominin face in the boxes. Berger halted the excavations while he and Steininger studied the skull and concluded that it was that of a robust ape-man. In May 2001 Berger resumed his work at Coopers A and within three weeks his team found another two robust molars, the first Coopers fossils to be recovered *in situ*.

Under their scrutiny Coopers began to yield more and more finds. Pieces of fossilized hominin, extinct animals and stone tools emerged. Coopers has now joined the ranks of the richest fossil-bearing sites in the Cradle of Humankind, and may well be the basis of another five decades of scientific investigation.

The history of Coopers demonstrates that there is probably still much to be discovered, not only at Coopers itself, but also at other sites in the Cradle of Humankind.

Coopers

Coopers is a relatively new fossil site situated between Sterkfontein and Kromdraai. In the 1930s a group of Wits students apparently found a hominin tooth at the site, but this has not been verified as the original specimen has gone missing. Although excavations at Coopers were resumed during the mid-1990s it was only in 2001 that valuable fossils began to emerge, including the molar of a robust australopithecine and the faunal remains of sabre-tooth cats and extinct pigs. During 2000 a box of breccia from Coopers housed at the Transvaal Museum was re-examined and found to contain the crushed facial bones of a robust ape-man.

Lee Berger and Lazarus Kgasi discuss one of the latest finds at Coopers.

THE CHANGING FACE OF EXCAVATION

Students, scientists and visitors assist in digging fossils from the ground at sites around the Cradle of Humankind, but day in and day out the people who do most of the work are the permanent field technicians.

The traditional role of a field technician as someone who merely carried breccia or wielded a pick has changed dramatically. Now, the field technicians are educated individuals, many pursuing higher degrees, who perform all the functions of a scientific assistant on site. From laser mapping using a theodolite, to fossil identification in the field and laboratory, the modern field technician is a trained, skilled, and critical part of the research team.

The number of women on site has also increased dramatically over the past few years, and most of the newer sites now boast at least 50 per cent gender equity.

Irene Maphofa *(foreground)* and Johannes Msetywa excavating the Coopers site.

OTHER PREHISTORIC SITES WITHIN THE CRADLE OF HUMANKIND

Bolt's Farm

Bolt's Farm is a series of small sites that have to date yielded only a single hominin tooth but a variety of animal fossils including the almost complete skeleton of a *Dinofelis* (extinct false sabre-tooth cat) that may have fallen to its death in one of the caves while stalking trapped baboons. Bolt's Farm is the only site in the Cradle of Humankind where modern elephant fossils have been found.

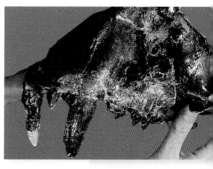

A *Dinofelis* skull from Bolt's Farm.

Uitkomst Cave

Uitkomst Cave in the John Nash Nature Reserve appears to have been inhabited on and off for at least 10 000 years. The Cave, discovered by archaeologist Revil Mason during the early sixties, is important for two main reasons:

- it shows the transition from the Later Stone Ages to the Iron Ages;
- it has a large variety of artefacts, including stone tools, shards of distinctive Tswana/Sotho pottery and the remains of smelting furnaces

The stone tools were found around the remains of a hearth where hunter-gatherers presumably roasted their meat or huddled together against the winter cold. The tools are scrapers and microliths associated with the San of the Later Stone Age.

The main Iron Age artefacts are two crude iron furnaces, the oldest being about 500 years old. The younger furnace was built on top of the older one. Traces of copper and iron have been found including the remains of copper bracelets. Analysis of the site suggests that during the Iron Ages Uitkomst was first used as a smelting centre and then much later as a dwelling.

The remains of pottery vary – they seem to be from bowls that were fairly deep with an average diameter of about 12 cm. Most of the rims are plain but some are ornately stamped and incised. They appear to be part of a single pottery tradition associated with the Later Iron Age in Gauteng and the northern Free State.

Other artefacts found at Uitkomst include the remains of reed mats held together by fibre strings, the remains of dry stone walling and a single cowrie shell that indicates that there was some contact with the east coast. The Uitkomst people were the ancestors of the BaFokeng who today occupy the platinum-rich area near Sun City to the west of the Cradle of Humankind.

Inside Wonder Cave.

Wonder Cave

Wonder Cave is a large underground cave that is believed to be approximately 2,2 million years old. Besides Sterkfontein it is the only site in the Cradle of Humankind that is regularly open to the public. It is a particularly good example of cave formation and the stalactites have escaped the destruction that has befallen most other caves in South Africa. The fossils of several baboons are preserved behind a flowstone curtain – they are believed to have fallen in from the narrow surface opening.

Motsetse

Motsetse is located in the Cradle Nature Reserve near Broederstroom. It was discovered in 1999 by Professor Lee Berger. Although no hominin fossils have yet been found at Motsetse, a number of primate and false sabre-tooth cat fossils have been unearthed. Tours and game drives can be organized from the nearby Cradle restaurant.

Haasgat

Haasgat is a site believed to be between 1 and 1,5 million years old. No hominin fossils have yet been found in the deposits but several baboon fossils have been found during excavations in the 1980s and 1990s. The remains of forest-dwelling monkeys have also been recovered here.

Minnaars

Minnaars site is a series of fossil-rich small caves between Kromdraai and Plover's Lake. Several small carnivore fossils have been found during intermittent excavations but no thorough fossil search of the site has yet been conducted.

Our ancestors climbed down from the trees and walked out into the savannah in response to their changing environment. This was a giant evolutionary leap in the history of humankind.

Maropeng Visitors' Centre

The Maropeng Visitors' Centre near Sterkfontein is the best place to learn about the Cradle of Humankind. Maropeng, the Setswana word for 'returning to our place of origins', consists of a huge domed structure – the Tumulus (which means burial mound) – which incorporates a state-of-the-art museum and visitor attraction centre. Visitors can explore the history of the Earth and humankind through interactive displays that include themes such as the discovery of fire, bipedalism, extinction and DNA. There is a large underground lake where tourists can take a boat ride to a 'virtual' cave, and a children's archaeological digging site. Other facilities include a shop, three restaurants, a conference centre, amphitheatre, boutique hotel and picnic site with wonderful views over the Magaliesberg.

The Maropeng Visitors' Centre houses an exhibit on the history of the Earth and humankind, and incorporates state-of-the art facilities.

Kevin Kuykendall with the *Paranthropus* tooth from Gondolin.

Gondolin

Gondolin has deposits similar to Swartkrans, namely between 1,5 and 2 million years old. A *Homo* tooth and a robust ape-man tooth have been found at the site.

IMPORTANT FOSSIL FINDS

NAME	SIGNIFICANCE	ESTIMATED AGE	DATE/ LOCATION
Sahelanthropus tchadensis (Toumai Skull) TM 266-01-060-1	One of the earliest hominin-like skulls found to date; very primitive features that cast doubt on whether it is part of the human lineage – may be ancestral to the gorilla	6-7 mya	2001 Chad
Orrorin tugenensis (Millennium Man)	Appears to be over a million years older than any other hominin yet discovered; if so, it places the creature at the point in time where the lineage split between ancestral hominins and apes	Approx 6 mya	2000 Kenya
Ardipithecus ramidus (ARA-VP)	Possible ancestor to australopithecines; fragments from 17 individuals show mixture of hominin and ape features	4,4 mya	1992 Ethiopia
Australopithecus anamensis (KP29281)	Fossilized tibia appears to be the oldest evidence of bi-pedalism	4 mya	1994 Kenya
Kenyathropus platyops (KNM WT 40000)	Flat-faced skull with australopithecine-sized brain but habiline features	3,3 mya	1999 Kenya
Australopithecus afarensis (Lucy) AL 288-1	Almost complete skeleton discovered of ape-man that shows human features beginning to overshadow ape-like features	3,2 mya	1973 Ethiopia
Australopithecus (Little Foot) (Stw 573)	As yet uncategorized hominin that may be the oldest australopithecine found in southern Africa	2,6-3,3 mya	1997 South Africa (Sterkfontein)
Australopithecus africanus (Taung Child)	First significant fossil find in Africa that suggested an intermediate species between humans and apes	2-3 mya	1926 Africa (Taung, N Cape)
Australopithecus africanus (Mrs Ples) Stw 5	First adult ape-man find in Africa that confirmed Dart's theories that Africa was humanity's ancestral home	2,5 mya	1947 South Africa (Sterkfontein)
Australopithecus garhi (BOU-VP 12/132)	Ape-man found in association with stone tools, but it is unclear as yet whether *A. garhi* made them	2,5 mya	1997 Ethiopia
Paranthropus aethiopicus (Black Skull) KNM-WT 17000	Complete cranium with puzzling mixture of ape and human features; East African version of robust ape-man	2,5 mya	1985 Kenya
Paranthropus robustus (Kromdraai Ape-Man) TM 1517	First robust ape-man found in southern Africa	1-2 mya	1938 South Africa (Kromdraai)
Paranthropus robustus (Eurydice and Orpheus) DNH 7 & 8	Male and female robust ape-man skulls found together – Eurydice is one of the most complete robust ape-man skulls found and the first robust female	1,5-2 mya	1994 South Africa (Drimolen)

NAME	SIGNIFICANCE	ESTIMATED AGE	DATE/ LOCATION
Homo rudolphensis KNMR–ER 1470	Possibly the earliest member of the genus *Homo*	1,9 mya	1972 Kenya
Paranthropus boisei (Nutcracker Man) OH 5	First robust ape-man to be found in East Africa – initially incorrectly thought to be part of modern human lineage	1,8 mya	1959 Tanzania
Homo habilis (OH 7-16)	Several skeletons found showing more modern morphology than australopithecines; believed to be part of our own genus	1,8 mya	1960 Kenya
Homo erectus/ergaster (Turkana Boy)	Fossil found of surprisingly tall young boy, which indicated a radical shift in morphology from australopithecines in a relatively short space of time	1,6 mya	1984 Kenya
Homo habilis (Stw 53)	Transitional species showing more modern traits than earlier *Homo*; found in association with stone tools	1,5 mya	1976 South Africa (Sterkfontein)
Homo erectus (Pinhead) OH 1	More modern human morphology but surprisingly smaller brain size than earlier *Homo* specimens	800 000– 1,2 mya	1962 Tanzania
Homo erectus (Java Man) Trinell 2	Initially thought to be the original human ancestor when discovered, leading scientists to believe Asia was the Cradle of Humankind	Approx 700 000 ya	1891 Indonesia
Homo sapiens Elandsfontein Skull	Transitional species between *Homo erectus* and *Homo sapiens*	400 000 ya	1953 South Africa (Cape West Coast)
Homo heidelbergensis (Florisbad Skull and Kabwe Man or Broken Hill Skull)	Also known as archaic *Homo sapiens*; possible ancestor to Neanderthals or *Homo sapiens*; prominent brow ridges; associated with Acheulean stone tools	Approx 200 000 ya	1932 South Africa (Free State) 1921: Zambia
Homo neanderthalensis (Neanderthal 1)	Neanderthals were physiologically modern hominins but with pronounced brow ridges; lived contemporaneously with *Homo sapiens sapiens*	Approx 50 000 ya	1856 Germany
Homo sapiens sapiens (Cro-Magnon Man)	The defining early skull of early *Homo sapiens sapiens*	Approx 30 000 ya	1868 France
Homo floresiensis The Hobbit (LB 1)	Remarkable hominin that took all scientists by surprise; anatomically modern but a tiny version of *Homo erectus*	18 000 ya	2003 Indonesia

This is not a comprehensive list of all the significant fossil finds in the last 150 years, but represents the major finds of different hominin species.
mya = millions of years ago

CHAPTER FIVE
A HOMININ WHO'S WHO

Human evolution is becoming an increasingly complicated science. Less than a century ago, scientists were concerned with finding the 'missing link' between apes and humans. Subsequent discoveries have made it clear that this is a misnomer, and that there are at least 13 intermediate species of early hominins separating ancestral apes from modern humans.

Although dating and analysis techniques have become increasingly sophisticated there is still no clear consensus on which species represent the direct chain of human evolution that eventually gave rise to *Homo sapiens*. In fact, each new discovery seems to present as many questions as answers, an issue complicated by the patchy and inconsistent fossil record.

Although South Africa and East Africa have been most conducive to the preservation of fossils, this does not necessarily mean that early hominin species were restricted to these areas or that important evolutionary steps didn't occur elsewhere in Africa. There appears to be growing scientific consensus that hominin evolution was triggered primarily by climatic change and that the physical adaptations of our ancestors were a response to a changing environment.

What has emerged as a possibility is that important evolutionary events may have taken place simultaneously in different geographical areas, and that many early hominins were unrelated variations of the same basic theme. This chapter contains a 'Who's Who' of the hominins we know of to date in the time sequence in which they are believed to have inhabited the Earth.

The story of hominin evolution is of course not restricted to southern Africa. It is a pan-African phenomenon that occurred outside the tropical evergreen forests where chimpanzees and gorillas evolved, taking place in the expanding savanna and broken woodland.

It is likely that the cooler climate of the Miocene triggered the evolutionary development of early hominins. Unfortunately very few fossils have been found from between 10 and 6 million years ago, which makes it difficult to establish exactly what creatures gave rise to our earliest ancestors, and what they looked like. The cooler climate led to a shrinking of the primates' familiar environment of the tropical rainforests and this affected their food sources.

Bipedalism is probably a consequence of the destruction of this original forest environment and the encroachment of the savanna grassland. Walking on two legs was also linked to having to travel greater distances for food.

Subsequent climatic changes prompted adaptations to the body shape and brain size of our earliest ancestors. The following section details the earliest hominins, although the exact relationship between them remains speculative.

SAHELANTHROPUS TCHADENSIS (7–6 MYA)

The discovery in Chad of a 6 to 7 million-year-old skull of *Sahelanthropus tchadensis*, dubbed the Toumai skull, has stirred debate among anthropologists over whether it is the oldest remnant of a pre-human ancestor or an ancient ape. The Toumai skull was announced by French scientists as the earliest human ancestor in July 2002. The

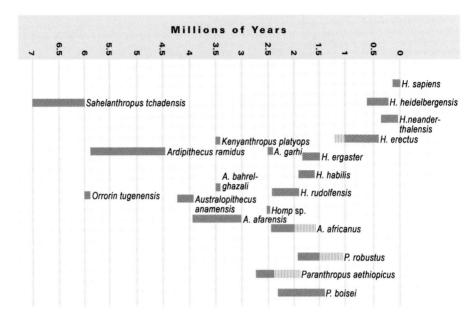

The position of hominin species in the fossil record of Africa. Shaded areas indicate the first and last known appearance of hominin species.

specimen has a thick brow and flat face and strong neck muscle markings. But other scientists say the skull is not on the human branch of the evolutionary tree, but may be that of a female gorilla or a chimpanzee, or a species that has since become extinct. More and better specimens will be required before the debate is settled.

ORRORIN TUGENENSIS (>6 MYA)

Dubbed the Millennium Man, this hominin was discovered in December 2000 in the Tugen Hills in Kenya's Lake Baringo district by a team led by Brigitte Senut and Martin Pickford. The remains include a femur, pieces of a jaw, some ape-like front teeth, human-like arm bones and a finger bone. Potentially the most dramatic fossil find in the last 20 years, it was designated *Orrorin tugenensis* (Original Man from Tugen).

The Millennium Man was significant because it appeared to be over a million years older than any other hominin discovered at the time. If this holds true, it places the creature at the point in time where the lineage split between ancestral hominins and apes.

Orrorin tugenensis appears to have been a biped with a relatively primitive head, but is unlike any other early hominid because it had ape-like front teeth, yet thickly enamelled, bulbous back teeth very much like those of later hominids.

ARDIPITHECUS RAMIDUS (5,8–4,4 MYA)

The fossil remains of at least 17 individuals of this genus were found in Ethiopia's Afar region by a University of Berkeley, California team led by Tim White and Yohannes Haile-Selassie over a number of field seasons beginning in 1991. The fossils, consisting mostly of teeth, skull pieces and upper limb bones, are highly fragmented, which makes analysis speculative.

The lack of complete lower limb remains means there is still uncertainty about whether *Ardipithecus ramidus* ('the ground ape representing the root') was capable of walking on two legs. White insists that the ankle bone fragments discovered show that it was bipedal, but also comfortable living in trees. Details of the finds have only recently been published, and until the scientific community has time to digest these results, the debate among scientists will continue as to whether this is in fact a hominin or merely an early hominoid, more related to living chimpanzees.

THE AUSTRALOPITHECINES

Between 4 and 1 million years ago, several different species of ape-men inhabited the African landscape. There appears to have been significant regional variation among these species, but two dominant forms have been identified:

- the gracile australopithecines, defined by their relatively 'light' masticating apparatus (their teeth and chewing muscles), an older species that disappeared from the fossil record between 2 and 2,5 million years ago, and
- the robust australopithecines (sometimes placed in the genus *Australopithecus*, but increasingly these days placed in the genus *Paranthropus*), who survived until about 1 million years ago before becoming extinct. They are labelled 'robust' not because of their body size, but because of the tremendous size of their jaws and teeth.

The biggest difference between the australopithecines and the chimpanzee-like creatures they are believed to have descended from is that the australopithecines could walk on two legs. The australopithecines also displayed a slight increase in cranial capacity, although they retained a relatively prognathic, or protruding, face.

It has recently become apparent that there were also various postcranial adaptations within the group. Some, for example, were more adapted to climbing, while others were more suited to a terrestrial lifestyle.

Australopithecus anamensis (4,2–3,8 mya)

The earliest of the australopithecines, this species is based on a relatively small number of specimens discovered by Meave Leakey's Kenya National Museum team in the Lake Turkana region of Kenya. A large tibia (shin bone) indicates that this species was well adapted to walking on two legs, while the parallel tooth rows visible in the jaws are more ape-like, indicating a very primitive head compared to the hominins listed below. This species looks like a good candidate as ancestor of all later hominins. Towards the end of the Miocene, the shrinking forests of Africa provided less and less habitable space for the apes, and they started to become extinct, a trend that continues today. At the same time, the more terrestrial, faster breeding monkeys began to increase, leading to the dominance of monkeys over apes in terms of numbers.

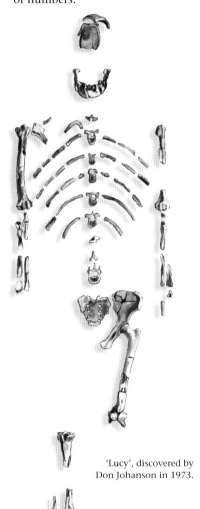

'Lucy', discovered by Don Johanson in 1973.

Australopithecus afarensis (3,8–3 mya)

One of the most widespread of the early hominins and probably the best documented because of the well-known 'Lucy' skeleton, *Australopithecus afarensis* (the southern Ape from Afar) was first discovered by Don Johanson in the Hadar region of Ethiopia in 1973. It was initially believed to be the root ancestor of all subsequent hominins.

More recent discoveries appear to rule this out, although there is an ongoing argument as to where *afarensis* should be placed in the human family tree. Characteristics of this species include sexual dimorphism (the males are larger than the females, much like gorillas), and a cranial capacity of around 400 cubic centimetres. Remains of this species have been found in Tanzania, Ethiopia and possibly Chad.

There has been a great deal of debate among scientists as to whether *afarensis* was arboreal or not. Recent discoveries indicate that the species was probably adapted to many different types of habitat. The famous Laetoli footprint trail, in which footprints 3,6 million years old have been preserved in ancient ash near a volcano in Tanzania, is attributed to this species.

Australopithecus bahrelghazali (3,5–3,0 mya)

This australopithecine was discovered in 1995 in North Africa by French palaeoanthropologist Michel Brunet. It has been suggested that it is a regional variant of *afarensis*. However, only parts of the skull have been found, so very little is known of the rest of the body.

Kenyanthropus platyops (3,5–3,0 mya)

A flat-faced ape man found in Kenya. This enigmatic new genus and species has been the focus of considerable debate concerning its position in human evolution.

Australopithecus africanus (3,1–2,1 mya)

The gracile ape-man *africanus* (the southern Ape of Africa) is represented by the fossils of the Taung child and Mrs Ples. This species is slightly more advanced than *afarensis*, with a larger cranial capacity and larger teeth. It is found at sites throughout South Africa and is particularly prevalent at Sterkfontein, but as yet it has not been found elsewhere in Africa. There is inconclusive evidence that *africanus* may have been the mother species for both the robust australopithecines and the early forms of *Homo*.

Africanus had longer arms and shorter legs than *afarensis*, which at first would suggest that it was more primitive. However, its facial characteristics are much more human-like and its brain was probably slightly bigger than *afarensis*. The average body weight of a male has been estimated at about 45,5 kg.

Their social organization was probably similar to that of chimpanzees. Their diet probably consisted of fruits and leaves, though recent isotopic studies have suggested that a significant quantity of meat was also eaten. They would most likely have been scavengers rather than hunters. They probably occupied open environments such as woodlands, and may have included some form of grasses or sedges in their diet. *Africanus* spent a significant amount of time in the trees, a conclusion supported by close observation of hand and foot bones.

Australopithecus africanus has been found only in Sterkfontein Member 4 and possibly Gladysvale, although fossils of this species are also known from Makapansgat and Taung.

Australopithecus garhi (2,4 mya)

The last of the 'definitive' australopithecines, this species is a recent addition to the genus *Australopithecus*. Discovered by Tim White's team in the Middle Awash region of Ethiopia, *garhi* appears to be more advanced than *afarensis*, displaying a mixture of both gracile and robust tendencies. Named after the Afar word for surprise, *garhi* has

WHO WERE THE FIRST TOOL MAKERS?

One of the most difficult questions facing scientists trying to interpret the behaviour of early hominins is: who made the tools found at the sites?

It had always been presumed that members of the genus *Homo*, with their bigger brains and more human-like bodies, were the makers of the stone and bone tools found at sites both in southern and East Africa.

However, recent work on the morphology of the robust australopithecines, and increasing discoveries of these more 'primitive' hominins in direct association with tools, mean that the robust ape-men cannot be excluded as possible tool users and makers.

Nevertheless, with no direct way of linking any single species to the tools recovered with their remains, and considering that practically every site in the right time range contains both *Homo* and *Paranthropus* remains, scientists are still a long way from discovering exactly which hominin made which tool.

been found in association with stone tools, but there is no evidence yet that it was capable of making tools. Fragmentary postcranial evidence suggests that *garhi* had both long arms and long legs, giving it unusual body proportions compared to other early hominins.

PARANTHROPUS (2,5–1,0 MYA)

Formerly classified as a robust form of *Australopithecus* but now more frequently put into the separate genus *Paranthropus*. *Paranthropus* fossils are characterized by massive teeth and jaw muscles, which indicate a low-nutrition vegetarian diet (lots of chewing to extract nutrients) that may have been an adaptation to the drier African environment 3 million years ago. Recent examinations of its hand bones have revealed that *Paranthropus* had the capability to manufacture and manipulate stone tools, which are often found in association with fossil remains. However, there is still no definitive evidence that *Paranthropus* or *Homo* made the tools found in the fossil sites in the Cradle of Humankind. *Paranthropus* had a relatively smaller brain than contemporaneous hominins in the genus *Homo*, but a slightly larger brain than the gracile australopithecines.

Paranthropus aethiopicus (2,6–2,2 mya)

Found in Kenya and Ethiopia, *aethiopicus* is suspected of being the common ancestor of the later paranthropines. The Black Skull, discovered in Kenya by Alan Walker in 1985, is the best fossil example of this species. It is the first species in the hominin fossil record to exhibit the massive teeth and chewing muscles that characterize the shift to a vegetarian lifestyle brought about by the aridification of Africa and the disappearance of the Miocene forests.

Paranthropus boisei (2,2–1,2 mya)

Producing some of the largest fossil representatives of the robust australopithecines, *boisei* epitomizes a 'hyper-robust' ape-man. With their huge teeth and massive jaws, males of this species are unmistakable, typically having bony crests atop their skulls just to support their massive jaw muscles. Relative to body size, they have the smallest hominin brain case recorded (less than 420 cc), although some individuals have cranial capacities in the low 500 cc range. The best known example is the 'Nutcracker Man' discovered by Mary and Louis Leakey at Olduvai Gorge in Tanzania in 1959 and given this name by Phillip Tobias. This specimen was also often referred to as 'Dear Boy', a play on the name *boisei*.

Paranthropus robustus (2,0–1,0 mya)

Robustus is the southern African version of the robust ape-men. Often called the flat-faced ape-man because of its dished-out facial area, it is the most common hominin in southern Africa and probably the best represented fossil hominin in the African record. The first robust australopithecine was discovered by Robert Broom at Kromdraai in 1938. Its main characteristics are powerfully developed facial muscles and bones. Although it was originally thought that this robusticity applied to the entire body, discoveries of bones have shown that they were not significantly larger than the gracile australopithecines, weighing about 47,7 kg.

SK48 (*P. robustus*), found at Swartkrans in 1948.

Their skulls had massive attachments for powerful chewing muscles. They also had enormous teeth, and clearly did a significant amount of heavy chewing. Their diet most likely consisted of tough, fibrous vegetation such as roots, tubers and roughage. They may also have supplemented this vegetarian diet with termites, as tools found at Swartkrans appear to have been employed to break open the mounds of these insects. *Paranthropus robustus* is endemic to South Africa, and they probably had a wide habitat tolerance, as remains have been found in both open grassland and more closed woodland environments.

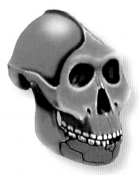
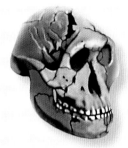
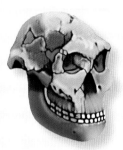
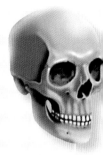

P. robustus (male)	*P. robustus* (female)	*P. boisei* (female)	*Homo sapiens sapiens*

LUMPERS VS. SPLITTERS

One of the problems in tracing the development of a new species is the gradation that takes place in between the definite changes of physical characteristics. It is therefore often difficult to decide on which side of the dividing line a species may be, or exactly where that dividing line lies. This is one of the problems faced by scientists categorizing hominins during the 3- to 2-million-year period when several species co-existed.

The debate around early *Homo* is particularly vociferous in this regard. Some scientists argue that *Homo habilis*, the much heralded 'first human' considered to have been the original maker of stone tools, was actually an australopithecine, and that a more correct appellation would be *Australopithecus habilis*.

The argument as to who falls in the genus *Homo* or not usually revolves around brain size, with 650 cc being the generally accepted dividing line. However, the more discoveries that are made, the more arbitrary this definition appears to be.

Because of the degree of variation among the early species of *Homo* discovered so far, scientists generally fall into one of two camps in their definitions:

● **The lumpers** – those who group *Homo* into three broad categories (*habilis*, *erectus* and *sapiens*) and downplay the significance of the variations within these categories, often by ascribing them to regional tendencies.

● **The splitters** – scientists who believe the variations are significant enough to warrant new species within the genus *Homo*, and that the fossil record so far indicates that early *Homo* consisted of a number of species (*habilis*, *rudolfensis*, *ergaster*, *erectus*, *heidelbergensis*, *antecessor*, *neanderthalensis* and *sapiens*).

The jury is still out on which approach is better. The only thing known for sure is that the record of early humanity is far more complicated than previously thought.

Remains of *P. robustus* have been discovered at Swartkrans Members 1–3, Kromdraai B, Drimolen, Coopers and Gondolin. They are not known anywhere outside the COH. The species existed from about 2 mya until approximately 1 mya.

EARLY HOMO (2,4–1,8 MYA)

The key difference between the australopithecines and the lumped group 'early *Homo*' is that the latter had a much larger and more complex brain that may be linked to tool-making abilities. Typically, we characterize early *Homo* by its more generalized skull, with no specialized adaptations such as sagittal crests or a flattened face. *Homo* species had less prominent brow ridges and a general reduction in facial prognathism. Early *Homo* species had smaller pre-molars and seemed to be omnivorous, adding substantially more meat to their diet than the mainly vegetarian australopithecines.

The earliest known fossil specimens have been dated to around 2,4 mya, and show generalized characteristics. They are found throughout Africa, and many have not been classified to species. *Homo habilis* and *H. rudolfensis* are two later types of 'confirmed' early *Homo* species, but even their status is sometimes questioned, with some palaeoanthropologists wanting to place them in the genus *Australopithecus*. In South Africa, early *Homo* fossils have been found at Sterkfontein, Coopers, Swartkrans and Drimolen.

Homo rudolfensis

Homo rudolfensis (est. 2,4–1,8 mya)

Rudolfensis was named after Lake Rudolph, the colonial name for Lake Turkana, where its fossilized remains were found by Richard Leakey in the late 1960s and early 1970s.

The argument for *rudolfensis* as a separate species is a tenuous one because of the lack of strong fossil evidence. Indeed, some scientists have rather unkindly described *rudolfensis* as a garbage-can species, consisting of all the 'throwaway' bits of fossils that can't be neatly ascribed to *habilis* or *ergaster*. It has affinities with many of the hominins, including *Homo habilis*, *H. ergaster* and *H. erectus*. It has been tentatively associated with simple flake tool technology. It is hypothesized that *H. rudolfensis* congregated near areas that offered many different food resources, such as lake margins, stream confluences and hills.

Homo habilis (2–1,6 mya)

With a larger brain than the australopithecines (around 650–800 cc), *Homo habilis*, meaning 'handy man', is the earliest species of hominin placed in the genus *Homo*. The first specimen was found by the Leakeys at Olduvai Gorge in 1960. The species is characterized by a rounder head, reduced prognathism, more human-like teeth and less pronounced brow ridges. Little is known about this species, mainly because there is disagreement about exactly which fossils can be ascribed to it, both in East and South Africa. It has been suggested that members of the species had the capacity for language, but this is difficult to confirm.

Fossil evidence suggests *habilis* was a small creature weighing approximately 40 kg and, like *africanus*, had longer arms in relation to its legs. Indeed this characteristic suggests that fossils attributed to *H. habilis* would be better placed in the genus *Australopithecus*, thus creating some doubt as to whether *habilis* was in fact the ancestor of *erectus*.

Habilis has long been associated with the crude Oldowan tool industry. It is possible that the earliest stone tools in Africa, found in Ethiopia and dated at 2,5 million years old, were produced by *H. habilis*, but there is too much controversy as to who the first tool makers were for this to be anything other than speculative.

Homo habilis has been recorded exclusively in Member 5 of Sterkfontein, but this identification is being questioned. It has also been found at Olduvai Gorge in Tanzania, as well as Koobi Fora in Kenya.

Homo ergaster and H. erectus (2 mya–400 000 BCE)

Homo ergaster is often used as a synonym for 'early African *Homo erectus*'. Around 2 million years ago, there was a dramatic shift in hominin cranial and postcranial morphology. *Homo erectus* can be regarded as the first easily identifiable true human ancestor. Reaching modern human stature, but with a brain approximately three-quarters the size of a modern human brain, the earliest *H. erectus* must have been a formidable creature on the African savanna.

The technology of *H. erectus* is epitomized by the handaxe, a generally enormous, teardrop-shaped bifacial tool. *Homo erectus* is the first hominin known to have left Africa. It developed the controlled use of fire, although the only evidence of this in Africa thus far can be found at Swartkrans in the Cradle of Humankind. By 700 000 to 1 million years ago, *erectus* was distributed throughout the Old World.

Most scientists agree that *Homo erectus* is the youngest direct ancestor of *H. sapiens* (though some recognize an intermediary stage, *H. heidelbergensis*; if correct, this view would distance *H. erectus* by one stage in evolution, but not remove it from our family tree). Being the first hominin species to move out of Africa, *Homo erectus* remains are therefore widespread throughout Africa, Europe, Asia and Indonesia. There is significant evidence that hunting and meat-eating were an important part of the everyday life of *H. erectus*. Almost certainly, *erectus* was able to communicate in some form of language. The species is known to have had a limited tool kit. They almost certainly had a wide habitat tolerance. Tantalizing evidence in Indonesia has raised the possibility that *H. erectus* was a capable woodworker.

It is now even suggested that in Indonesia, *H. erectus* developed some level of sea-faring or rafting capabilities that enabled them to travel between islands. To this day it remains something of a mystery as to how the Indonesian islands were originally inhabited by early *H. erectus*. Stone tool evidence from islands that were never connected by land bridges indicates that these remote archipelagos were occupied. *H. erectus* must have either swum, rafted or boated across the waters to reach these islands. What could have motivated them to undertake such a perilous step into the unknown is a matter of speculation.

This *Homo erectus* skull of a boy from Nariokotome, Kenya, is part of one of the most complete hominin skeletons recovered to date.

Homo erectus or *ergaster* remains have been recovered from Swartkrans Members 1 and 2, Drimolen, Coopers and possibly Gondolin, as well as numerous localities in East Africa. This species first appeared in Africa about 1,8 mya, and it probably vanished about 1 mya in South Africa, though it may have survived slightly longer than this estimate.

Homo antecessor (1,0 mya–800 000 BCE)

This variation of early *Homo* is restricted to southern Europe and possibly North Africa. *Antecessor* had a relatively 'modern' looking face, but with features of *erectus* in the cranium and later Neanderthals in the nasal region. It had a cranial capacity of around 1 000 cc. *Homo antecessor* is a good candidate ancestor of *H. heidelbergensis* and then

STONE TOOLS – THE DAWN OF TECHNOLOGY

The earliest stone tools discovered so far are from the Gona area in Ethiopia, and are believed to date back to approximately 2,5 million years ago. The appearance of stone tools has been linked to the development of our own genus, *Homo*. However, the Gona tools predate by 100 000 years the earliest *Homo* specimens found so far, which suggests either that an earlier form of *Homo* still remains to be found, or that the australopithecines like *Australopithecus garhi* were capable of making stone tools.

Stone tools are categorized into 'cultures' depending on how they were made or used. The basic categories are:

- **Oldowan** – a crude and limited stone tool kit associated with the Early Stone Age, and named after the Olduvai Gorge site in Tanzania where the first examples were found.
- **Acheulean** – a more refined and complicated tool kit that developed during the Early Stone Age (1,6 mya) and lasted until approximately 250 000 years ago, named after the French site of Saint Acheul.
- **Later Stone Age** – this continued in Africa far longer than it did in Europe; these tools are more specialized and more diverse than the earlier tool technologies.

The Cradle of Humankind contains a representative sample of almost all stone tool types manufactured by humans and their ancestors over the last 2 million years in Africa.

The Oldowan tools found in the Cradle of Humankind date back to approximately 2 million years ago and have been found at sites such as Sterkfontein Member 5 and recently at the Coopers site. These tools are really just flakes, the result of reducing a large stone to a smaller stone, and show little if any control over the end design. Included in the Oldowan culture are simple hammer-stones, which may have been nothing more than readily available river cobbles.

The more advanced tools of the Acheulean industry have been found at Swartkrans, and in the river gravels around the Cradle Nature Reserve. They are believed to date back to approximately 1,5 million years ago. The core element of the Acheulean tool kit is the handaxe. This bifacial, teardrop-shaped tool was the early Pleistocene equivalent of the Swiss Army knife, and was used for just about any task *Homo erectus*, the presumed maker of the Acheulean industry, might have wished to accomplish.

An example of Middle Stone-Aged flake technology.

Examples of stone tools from the Later Stone Age.

The Acheulean industry shows that deliberate choice was introduced into the tool-making process, from the raw material to the 'style' of the end product. It is the most enduring tool culture in history, existing for well over a million years with little variation. The same templates have been found across the world, from Africa to Europe and Asia. The Acheulean ended only about 250 000 years ago, which may be associated with the rise of archaic *H. sapiens* who, with a bigger brain size and more developed communication skills, developed a new kind of tool industry.

At sites such as Swartkrans and Plover's Lake, one can see evidence of flake industries and prepared core industries. This is a period that is termed the 'Middle Stone Age' in southern Africa. Points and blades began to appear and some of the finely crafted stone tools were hafted onto spears. In the coastal regions of southern Africa, new evidence is emerging that the Middle Stone Age was characterized by a technological complexity never before realised, with bone points and even artwork appearing contemporaneously with what used to be considered 'primitive' human technologies.

The timing of the transition from Middle Stone Age to Later Stone Age is complex, with evidence that in some areas 'modern' complex tools and culture appeared very early, while in other areas the transition from Middle Stone Age behaviour to the modern 'infinite' tool kit and behaviour may have occurred as recently as 20 000 years ago. Early and Middle Stone Age tools were characterized by their limitations – they were used essentially for bludgeoning, scraping, and cutting. The evolution of modern human behaviour saw the emergence of a far more complex tool kit, with stone, bone and wooden tools having an infinite variety of uses, from stitching clothing to harpooning fish. Later Stone Age tools were also influenced by an aestheticism that was not prevalent in early tool cultures, reflecting the increasing sophistication of evolving human interaction. Later Stone Age tools used by the San hunter-gatherers are microlithic and far more specialized than Early and Middle Stone Age tools.

The evidence for Later Stone Age occupation of the Cradle of Humankind is extensive. Almost every cave has some evidence of modern human occupation, and microlithic tools are widespread.

H. neanderthalensis. Its remains have been found at La Sima de los Huesos, near Atapuerca in Northern Spain, preserved in a deep cave. The bodies of at least six individuals may have been deposited there in ritual burial.

Homo heidelbergensis (600 000–200 000 BCE)

As tall as or even taller than modern humans and more robustly built, *Homo heidelbergensis* was probably the precursor of the Neanderthals in Europe, and the possible ancestor of *H. sapiens* in Africa. Archaeological evidence shows that this species was capable of group-hunting large game. Scrape marks on bones, indicating de-fleshing, may be a sign of cannibalism. There is a great deal of confusion as to whether the large robust human fossils found in Africa from this time period are members of this species or something different. Very large human remains have been found in southern Africa that have tentatively been attributed to *H. heidelbergensis*. These remains are mostly from the Cape coast.

The first fossil of an early human ancestor to be found in Africa, this skull of *H. heidelbergensis* was discovered in 1921.

Homo neanderthalensis (230 000–29 000 BCE)

Neanderthals appear to have evolved out of *Homo antecessor*, and were adapted to living in very cold climates. Their bodies were stocky and their nasal passages were adapted for processing icy air. First discovered in 1856 in the Neander Tal (valley) in Germany, Neanderthals shared many cultural and behavioural traits with modern humans. They seem to have been restricted initially to Europe, where they survived a series of ice ages over the last several hundred thousand years. However, it appears that later adaptations allowed them to live in temperate climates. Their remains have also been found in the Middle East, Asia and North Africa.

Homo sapiens (600,000 years ago to 200,000 years ago)

A great deal of scientific debate continues around the categorization of 'Archaic *Homo sapiens*', the forerunners of our own species, *H. sapiens sapiens*. Generally, the label applies to a variety of southern African fossil remains dated between 600 000 and 200 000 years ago, which is

OUT OF AFRICA

Africa gave the world humankind. It is scientifically uncontested that the earliest hominins developed in Africa and that *Homo erectus* led the first wave of migrations into the rest of the world approximately 1,8 million years ago. *Erectus* populations soon established themselves in most of the habitable areas in Europe and Asia.

There are two main schools of thought as to how modern humans originated:

- The multi-regional hypothesis holds that *H. sapiens sapiens* evolved regionally from the *erectus* populations distributed throughout the world. The implication is that Chinese *H. sapiens* had a fundamentally different origin from African *H. sapiens* and that differences between people are more biologically than culturally entrenched.

- The out-of-Africa hypothesis postulates that *H. sapiens* developed in Africa and then migrated from the continent, gradually replacing *H. erectus* populations in the rest of the world because of their superior technology and communication skills.

Modern genetic research increasingly supports the out-of-Africa hypothesis, showing that there is a greater genetic diversity among Africans than between Africans and other populations. Fundamentally, this means that Africans are 'older' and other race groups 'younger'. Geneticists believe that we are all descended from a population of modern *H. sapiens* that lived somewhere in Africa approximately 100 000 years ago.

Archaeological evidence suggests that an 'African Eve' lived in southern Africa. Nowhere else in the world is there a comparable record of evolutionary development demonstrating how *H. erectus* evolved into an archaic form of *H. sapiens*, which became refined into modern *H. sapiens*.

Many scientists believe modern humans migrated from Africa along the Rift Valley and over a land bridge into the Middle East and beyond.

One of the plausible theories on the origin of modern humans is that a sustainable population of archaic *sapiens* was cut off from the African interior by the expansion of the Kalahari and Karoo deserts around 200 000 years ago. This group found itself trapped in the narrow coastal plains between the Atlantic and the mountains on the edge of the desert. This is why their food consumption became increasingly marine-focused. Their diet of shellfish, mussels and fish, with its high protein levels, may have contributed to the development of the modern human brain.

the bridging period between the existence of *H. erectus* and the appearance of modern humans. A handful of fossils, including the Florisbad skull from the Free State, the Elandsfontein skull from the Cape West Coast and Kabwe Man (formerly known as the Broken Hill skull) from Zambia, have been classified as this transitional species, which appears to have slightly more primitive facial features compared to modern humans, including a more pronounced brow line. Archaic *H. sapiens* probably displayed the same capacity for complex social behaviour as early modern humans. It appears that there may be remains of archaic humans from Plover's Lake in the COH.

Homo sapiens sapiens (200 000 years ago to present)

Genetic evidence and the fossil record point to an African origin for modern humans. Modern *Homo sapiens* appears to have evolved from an archaic form that in turn evolved from *H. erectus*. Genetic evidence from examinations of both mitochondrial DNA (from the female line) and Y chromosome DNA (from the male line) adds support to the hypothesis that modern humans arose in Africa between 100 000 and 200 000 years ago. Modern humans reached Europe and, via coastal routes, Indonesia and Australia by around 50 000–60 000 years ago. Until recently, it was believed that modern human behaviour, characterized by the production of art, the burial of the dead and a complex tool kit, was a relatively recent, European phenomenon attributable only to Cro-Magnon man (an early type of *H. sapiens*) around 25 000–35 000 years ago. However, recent discoveries in Africa suggest that the earliest evidence of all these 'modern' attributes can be found in coastal sites and sites in East Africa more than 100 000 years earlier.

Homo floresiensis (18 000 years ago)

One of the enigmas of hominin evolution has been the recent discovery of the 'Hobbit', a dwarf form of *Homo erectus* discovered on the Indonesian island of Flores. The discovery at Liang Bua Cave by an Australian/Indonesian team in 2003 came as a complete surprise to almost all scientists studying human origins. Conventional wisdom is that hominins have grown in stature in more recent times. Yet the remains of a skull and a partial skeleton consisting of leg bones, parts of the pelvis, hands and feet, and some other fragments indicate that until relatively recently there existed what appears to be a dwarf species of *Homo erectus*. LB1, as the Hobbit specimen is scientifically known, was a female adult, about a metre tall with an extremely small brain of 417 cc. The skull has human-like teeth with a receding forehead and no chin. The fossil is 18 000 years old and was found near stone tools.

CHAPTER SIX

EXTINCT MAMMALS OF THE CRADLE OF HUMANKIND

The Cradle of Humankind provides a window into the past not only for understanding our own ancestors but those of other members of the animal kingdom. The far-reaching climatic changes in Africa during the past 5 million years triggered evolutionary adaptations among all species inhabiting the continent, not just among hominins.

The aridification of Africa saw the widespread encroachment of the savannah into areas that were previously heavily wooded forests. This shift in the environment radically affected the sources of food and those animals that could not adapt their diets to the spreading grasslands were faced with extinction. The climatic shifts associated with the Pliocene (5 mya to 1,6 mya) and the Pleistocene (1,6 mya to the present) led to drier conditions with far more erratic weather conditions. These conditions favoured collective rather than individual behaviour among animals and many of the 'loners' of the Miocene did not survive.

However, within this general aridification trend there were wet cycles in which the Gauteng highveld was almost subtropical in nature. The number and variety of animal fossils found at sites in the COH are testimony to the drama of evolutionary change on the African continent.

EXTINCT MAMMALS

The following mammals exist only as fossilized remains in the Cradle of Humankind. Therefore, this guide is intended as a general overview of these mammals and their evolutionary history.

Hominins

The COH has provided important evidence of the evolution of hominins for the last 2,5 million years. They are represented by members of the genus *Homo* as well as the genus *Australopithecus*. The genus *Australopithecus* can be traced as far back as 4,1 million years in Kenya. These earliest representatives of *Australopithecus* were already fully bipedal, though they were still characterized by small cranial capacities. *Australopithecus africanus* from Sterkfontein shows some of the same adaptations to bipedalism, and has been referred to by some as the direct, lineal ancestor to our own genus, *Homo*. Although very rare in the fossil assemblages of the COH, a number of specimens of *Homo* have also been found, providing significant insight into the evolution of our ancestors. Details of the hominins found in the Cradle of Humankind are dealt with in the 'A Hominin Who's Who' section, Chapter Five. They are: *Australopithecus africanus*; *Paranthropus robustus*; *Homo habilis*; *Homo erectus* and archaic *Homo sapiens*.

Homo habilis

Non-hominin primates

The fossilized remains of non-hominin primates of the COH comprise several species of extinct baboons and monkeys. Baboons first appeared in the late Miocene, probably 7–5 mya. There is a good fossil record of the various species. It is difficult to determine the precise evolutionary history of the baboons in southern Africa, but the oldest specimens of *Papio* (the genus of modern baboons) are to be found at Sterkfontein. The extinct baboons of southern Africa were mostly omnivorous and terrestrial.

Hamadryas baboon *Papio hamadryas robinsoni*

Originally accorded status as a separate species, *robinsoni* is now classified as a subspecies of the modern hamadryas baboon. Although the hamadryas baboon still exists today, it is no longer found in southern Africa, being restricted to the semi-desert Horn of Africa. In the past this was one of the most common baboons in the COH.

Papio hamadryas robinsoni fossils are known from Swartkrans Members 1–3, Kromdraai A and B, Coopers, Bolt's Farm, Schurweburg, Gladysvale and Drimolen. This subspecies probably arose in South Africa some 2 mya, and disappeared sometime in the Pleistocene.

Extinct large baboon *Papio (Dinopithecus) ingens*

The genus *Dinopithecus* was recently placed in the *Papio* genus because of the close similarities between the two types of baboon. This baboon is notably larger than modern baboons. Body size estimates place the largest specimens (presumably males) at more than 40 kg. Significant sexual dimorphism is evident in the cheek teeth of this species. The shape of the skull and teeth is so similar to that of modern savannah baboons that we can presume they shared behaviour patterns. *Papio ingens* probably consumed a similar diet, including grasses, leaves, roots and fruits. The cheek pouches of this species were slightly different from those of modern baboons, suggesting there was some difference in feeding behaviour.

This species is known from the Hanging Remnant and the Lower Bank of Member 1 at Swartkrans, and from Coopers and Kromdraai A. As such, its known time span is somewhat limited to approximately 1,8–1,5 mya.

Extinct gelada baboon *Theropithecus oswaldi*

This species of large, extinct baboon is closely related to the modern gelada baboon, found today in Ethiopia. *Theropithecus oswaldi* were much larger than their modern relatives, weighing in the neighbourhood of 40 kg. They probably had a diet similar

Extinct gelada baboon

to that of modern geladas, dedicated savannah grazers that subsist on a diet of grass and grass seeds. Their adaptation to terrestrialism is the most developed of all the non-hominin primates.

The teeth of *T. oswaldi* were high-crowned to cope with excessive wear from eating grass. Their third molars erupted relatively late in life so that when the earlier molars were wearing down, the third molars were just beginning to wear, prolonging the potential life span of the teeth in a fashion similar to elephants. Modern geladas have the most opposable thumb of all primates except humans. This provides them with a precision grip, as well as the ability to dig for rhizomes, roots and tubers during the dry season. The finger bones of *T. oswaldi* from Swartkrans appear similar to those of modern geladas. The social grouping of modern geladas consists of one-male harems and groups of bachelors banding together into groups of 50 to 250 individuals, although they sometimes number up to 600. It seems likely that the extinct form would have had a similar social organization.

Theropithecus oswaldi is known from Members 1–3 at Swartkrans and from Gladysvale and Coopers. Elsewhere in Africa fossils of *Theropithecus* dominate primate faunas from the late Pliocene until the mid to late Pleistocene, when they began to be replaced by savannah baboons (*Papio*).

Extinct small baboon *Parapapio jonesi*

Of the Plio-Pleistocene baboons found in southern Africa, the genus *Parapapio* is the most primitive. There are actually four species assigned to this extinct genus, although there is some question as to the actual separation of the groups, since the main criterion for distinguishing the species is molar size. *Parapapio jonesi* is the smallest of the *Parapapio* species, with an estimated body weight of approximately 18 kg. *Parapapio jonesi* was probably a fruit and leaf eater, and its limb bones suggest it was arboreal. It was most likely adapted to forested environments.

Parapapio species are known from Sterkfontein Member 4, Swartkrans Member 1 and Kromdraai A. They range in time in South Africa from 3–1 mya. Several extinct species of *Parapapio* are known in East Africa, the oldest of which are more than 4 million years old. It is possible that *Parapapio* could represent the ancestral African baboon.

Extinct colobus monkey *Cercopithecoides williamsi*

The only true monkey found in the Sterkfontein valley caves, this species was actually a colobine, or leaf-eating, monkey. They were large monkeys, weighing approximately 13 kg. Living colobine monkeys are arboreal, restricted to evergreen forest areas in equatorial Africa. The extinct monkey *Cercopithecoides* may have been able to live in less thickly wooded areas than are necessary for their closest living relatives, and were probably somewhat more terrestrial. The chewing muscles in *Cercopithecoides* were less powerfully developed than in modern colobines, but the teeth that have been found are often heavily worn. This suggests they were more likely to have eaten softer, grittier items, such as fruit and leaves, than modern colobines.

Cercopithecoides is known from the late Pliocene until the middle Pleistocene throughout Africa. Fossils have been recovered from Sterkfontein Member 4, the Lower Bank of Member 1 at Swartkrans, Member 2 at Swartkrans, Kromdraai B, Gladysvale and Drimolen. *Cercopithecoides* is also known from Makapansgat. It thus existed in South Africa from about 3 mya until just under 1,5 mya.

Extinct colobus monkey

Large felids

The large cats found in the fossil caves of the COH can be divided into two groups: the sabre-tooth cats and the false sabre-tooth cats. The sabre-tooth cats found in the COH belong to the subfamily Machairodontinae, and are typified by remarkably enlarged upper canines and reduced lower canines. These cats were the first successful large felid predators, overshadowing other carnivores from the Oligocene until their extinction in the Pliocene. The false sabre-tooth cats are characterized by the genus *Dinofelis*, the oldest representative of which is found at Langebaanweg on the Cape West Coast.

Extinct sabre-tooth cats
Homotherium crenatidens

These largest of the South African cats possessed the typically enlarged canine teeth that define sabre-tooth cats. The enlarged upper canines were serrated on both edges, and were almost delicately thin. The carnassial teeth were especially well adapted to slicing meat, but they would have had very little bone-cracking ability. The body size estimated for *Homotherium* is around 215 kg, which would have made them larger than modern male lions. These cats had powerfully built bodies, and would have been able to take down the largest of prey.

When hunting they most probably employed a stabbing technique, driving their large canines into the soft parts of their prey and then using a slicing motion to eviscerate them. It has been suggested that *Homotherium* may have hunted co-operatively in prides, perhaps as a mechanism to penetrate the protective shield walls adult Proboscideans form around their young when threatened. They were almost certainly the top predators until they became extinct. It is unlikely that *Homotherium* was a major threat to the hominins in the COH, since primates are particularly bony animals and any attack on such an animal would risk serious damage to their enlarged canines. *Homotherium's* large size, postcranial anatomy and presumed prey preferences indicate that these large cats would have preferred more open habitats as opposed to woodlands.

Homotherium crenatidens

Homotherium is known only from Bolt's Farm and Kromdraai A in the COH, though it is also known from the grey breccia of Makapansgat, as well as E Quarry at Langebaanweg. It therefore existed from the Pliocene until the mid-Pleistocene (5–1,5 mya).

Megantereon cultridens

Similar to Homotherium, Megantereon also had the specialized upper canine teeth that mark the Machairodontinae. However, Megantereon did not have serrated sabre-teeth, though their canines were recurved, with very sharp edges. The carnassial teeth in Megantereon were also specifically adapted to the slicing of meat, and not the cracking of bone. It is possible that their stouter canine teeth would have been used to pierce the hides of thick-skinned ungulates, causing significant trauma and blood loss in their victims.

Megantereon were smaller sabre-tooth cats, weighing approximately the same as a large female lion (150 kg). They probably favoured more closed habitats, but would have been capable of taking larger prey than modern felids such as leopards and lions, although their skeletons were clearly not adapted for fast movement. It has been suggested that Megantereon dragged prey into trees much like leopards, but such behaviour would have posed a significant risk of damage to their canines from transporting heavy loads, and is therefore unlikely.

Megantereon cultridens

Megantereon is known from Sterkfontein Members 4 and 5, the Hanging Remnant of Swartkrans and perhaps Members 2 and 3, Kromdraai A and B and Coopers. The earliest appearance of this genus is at Langebaanweg at 5 mya, and it survived until just over 500 000 years ago.

Extinct false sabre-tooth cat Dinofelis piveteaui

Dinofelis species lacked the elongated, curved canines of the Machairodontinae, and are therefore placed within the Felinae. This is why they are referred to as false sabre-tooth cats. Their canine teeth were somewhat elongated, though not as remarkably as in the sabre-tooth cats. They were also much stouter, similar to lions, but significantly larger. The estimated body size of Dinofelis was probably in the neighbourhood of 150 kg, similar to a large female lion. Dinofelis ranged from Europe, through East Africa and into South Africa. Their preferred habitat was probably a more closed environment, and their behaviour is hypothesized to have been rather similar to that

Dinofelis

of leopards. They are thus thought to have been solitary, nocturnal predators. Whether they preyed upon the hominins in the area is uncertain. Their larger body size and enhanced prey-grappling abilities would probably have allowed them to take larger prey than leopards quite regularly. *Dinofelis* would have had some tree-climbing ability, though its large size would have been a limiting factor. It has been suggested that Dinofelis may occasionally have scavenged carcasses dragged into trees by leopards. Their large size and powerful build would have made them one of the top predators in the Plio-Pleistocene.

Dinofelis are found in Sterkfontein Member 4, the Hanging Remnant and Member 2 of Swartkrans, Kromdraai A, Drimolen, Gladysvale, Motsetse and Bolt's Farm. They are also found in Langebaanweg, from about 5 mya, as well as in East Africa. By about 1 mya this genus had gone extinct.

Hyenas

During the Plio-Pleistocene, several types of hyena roamed the COH, about half of which became extinct. Hyenas may have developed their advanced bone-cracking abilities to process the carcasses that the sabre-tooth cats, with their exclusively meat-slicing teeth, left behind. Extinction in one part of a food web will affect other parts of the ecosystem, and it has been hypothesized that when the sabre-tooth cats went extinct, some of the hyenas followed suit, since the carcasses they depended on were no longer available.

Extinct giant hyena *Pachycrocuta brevirostris*

This extinct giant hyena was large, weighing just under 100 kg. The genus was very widely distributed through Africa and Eurasia. They probably avoided forested and closed areas, preferring more open grasslands and woodlands. The large size and powerful build of *Pachycrocuta* would have enabled it to process the largest of carcasses, and access the contents of bones that other hyenas simply could not. It has been suggested that *Pachycrocuta* may have operated in clans, which would have made them formidable predators on the Plio-Pleistocene landscape. Their extinction has been linked to the demise of the sabre-tooth cats. Once these felid super-predators had vanished, the large carcasses they produced would no longer have been available for *Pachycrocuta* to scavenge. The giant hyena would then have had to compete directly with the smaller hyenas for smaller carcasses. *Pachycrocuta* is known from Sterkfontein Members 4 and 5, Kromdraai A, Coopers and Gladysvale. It is also known from Makapansgat, extending its time range in South Africa from about 3 mya until about 1,5 mya. The genus survived in Eurasia until about 0,5 mya, and may thus have been present in Africa until that time.

Extinct giant hyena

Extinct hunting hyena *Chasmaporthetes nitidula*

Chasmaporthetes have been referred to as long-legged hunting hyenas. They were considerably smaller than the giant hyena, with an estimated body weight of 40 kg. This genus was widely distributed through Africa and Eurasia. The long legs of these animals suggest they were more adapted to running than modern hyenas, and may have engaged in more active hunting. Their teeth do not show the same specialization for bone crushing as those of modern hyenas, and they were probably about as adept at this task as large felids. *Chasmaporthetes* may have been pack animals, and their meat-slicing tactics may have left significant scavengable carcasses in the palaeo-environment.

    Chasmaporthetes are known from Sterkfontein Members 2, 4 and 5 as well as Swartkrans Members 1–3. They may also be derived from Member 2 at Sterkfontein, giving them a time range of over 3 mya until about just over 1 mya, when they vanished from southern Africa. In East Africa and Eurasia *Chasmaporthetes* existed over 4 mya.

Extinct hunting hyena

Canids

The fossil canids of the COH are only poorly understood, having been eclipsed by the more spectacular felids and hyaenids. It is becoming apparent that many more types of canid were present in the fossil caves than have been recognized to date.

Extinct wolf-like dog *Lycaon esabagyus*

This recently discovered species of wild dog may represent the oldest evidence for wild dogs in South Africa. It was a large animal, approximately the size of a modern North American wolf. It probably had an omnivorous diet, as a seed from a wild date palm was found in its abdominal cavity. So far it has only been recovered from Gladysvale, and is estimated to be just under 1 million years old.

Extinct wolf-like dog

Proboscideans and Hyracoids

The Proboscidea are animals with a mobile proboscis, or nose, such as elephants and their extinct ancestors. In what appears to be an absurd twist of nature, hyraxes, or dassies, are closely related to elephants.

Extinct elephant *Elephas recki*

The extinct elephant was slightly smaller than modern elephants. It differed from modern elephants in having smaller tusks and reduced premaxillae, the bones in which the tusks grow. The face of *Elephas recki* was more compressed, and the back of the skull was larger compared to modern elephants. *Elephas recki* is known from East and South Africa. This species of elephant probably had a diet similar to that of modern elephants, consisting of both browse and graze. Virtually all the remains in the COH fossil sites are of juveniles.

Elephant

Elephas recki is known from Sterkfontein Member 4, Swartkrans Members 1 and 3, and Gladysvale. It is probable that it existed at Makapansgat as well, giving it a time range of 3–1 mya in South Africa. It had a similar time span in East Africa.

Extinct giant hyrax *Procavia transvaalensis*

This species of extinct hyrax was about one-and-a-half times the size of modern rock hyraxes, or dassies, weighing an estimated 6,5–7 kg. Other than the size difference, *Procavia transvaalensis* was very similar to modern hyraxes. It can therefore be presumed that it had a similar diet and lifestyle. The species was originally named for a large hyrax recovered from Coopers in 1936. Many of the crania known from sites such as Swartkrans show evidence suggesting that it was eaten by leopards and eagles, much the same as today.

Extinct giant hyrax

Procavia transvaalensis is known from Sterkfontein Members 4 and 5, Swartkrans Members 1–3, Kromdraai A and probably B, Gladysvale, Coopers, Motsetse and Bolt's Farm. It is also known from Makapansgat, which suggests that it occurred in South Africa from 3 mya until its disappearance sometime in the Pleistocene.

Equids

Horses have a long evolutionary history, extending back as far as the Miocene in Africa. The equids can be divided into two basic groups in southern African fossil sites: the three-toed *Hipparion* and the single-toed *Equus*. *Hipparion* is the more primitive form, first appearing in the Miocene and surviving until the end of the Pleistocene, at which point it went extinct. The more advanced *Equus* first appeared in the Pliocene of North Africa, and soon after that in southern Africa. The genus *Equus* is of special importance for dating the fossil localities in Africa, since the genus first appeared about 2,4 mya in Africa. Therefore, any fossil locality containing *Equus* cannot be older than 2,4 million years. Equids are rare fossils in the COH.

Extinct Cape horse *Equus capensis*

Equus capensis, the giant Cape horse, was first described by Broom in 1909 based on fossils recovered near Cape Town. This horse was significantly larger than modern zebras, weighing an estimated 895 kg. Its skeleton was differently proportioned to that of modern zebras, as it had a more powerfully built, but shorter, body, and a more massive head. *Equus capensis* had a wide distribution, having been recovered from sites across southern and East Africa. Its social organization was probably very

Extinct Cape horse

similar to that of modern zebras. Its diet can be reconstructed to have been predominantly graze, as is the case with all members of the genus *Equus*.

Equus capensis has been recovered from Sterkfontein Member 4, Swartkrans Members 1–3, Kromdraai A, Gladysvale and Coopers. It made its last appearance at Equus Cave near Taung, in early Holocene times.

Extinct three-toed horse *Hipparion lybicum*

The three-toed *Hipparion* is the most primitive horse in the COH. The three toes on each foot were fully functional, whereas in *Equus* only the third toe bears weight, with the other toes reduced in size to useless 'splint' bones. *Hipparion* is estimated to have been larger than modern zebras, weighing approximately 489 kg. Its remains can be found throughout East Africa, indicating it was widely distributed in Africa. *Hipparion* was most likely a grassland grazer and quite water dependent.

Hipparion lybicum can be found in Swartkrans Members 1–3, Kromdraai A and possibly at Gladysvale.

Suids

The evolution of suids in Africa has been studied intensively for several decades. As a group, suids tend to evolve at a rapid rate, and thus are very important for biostratigraphic comparisons between the well-dated East African fossil deposits and the less securely dated South African ones. It is therefore unfortunate that suids are exceedingly rare in the fossil assemblages of the COH. The only exception is the newly opened site of Coopers, which has already produced a wealth of fossil suids. The oldest ancestors of the Suidae existed during the Oligocene, though the ancestry of the suids found in South Africa is much more recent. The 'common' fossil suid in South Africa, *Metridiochoerus*, has its origins at around 1,8 mya.

Extinct pig *Metridiochoerus andrewsi*

Metridiochoerus resembled modern warthogs, except that their tusks were essentially straight, projecting laterally from the sides of the muzzle. They were larger than warthogs, probably weighing in excess of 120 kg. They were most likely grazers, probably living in the open, watered areas also preferred by modern warthogs.

Extinct pig

Metridiochoerus andrewsi is known from Swartkrans Members 1–3, Kromdraai A, Coopers and Bolt's Farm in the COH. It is also known from Makapansgat around 3 mya, as well as Elandsfontein at 0,5 mya.

Giraffes

Extinct short-necked giraffe *Sivatherium maurusium*

The short-necked giraffe *Sivatherium* is the largest and most massive giraffe that ever existed in Africa, weighing up to 2 000 kg. *Sivatherium* probably lived in similar habitats to modern giraffes, ranging from savannahs to woodlands. Isotopic studies of their fossils show that this giraffe was a dedicated browser, and may have been more dependent on water than modern giraffes. It may also have fed at a lower level than modern giraffes.

Extinct short-necked giraffe

Sivatherium maurusium was initially known in the COH from a single deciduous tooth in Member 2 of Swartkrans, though recent examination of faunal collections has revealed giraffid postcranial remains in all members of Swartkrans. It has also recently been found at Coopers. Elsewhere in South Africa, this species is known from Makapansgat and Langebaanweg, as well as the Pleistocene sites of Florisbad, Cornelia and Elandsfontein. This species was thus present in South Africa from approximately 5 mya until as recently as 0,4 mya.

Bovids

Bovids are typically the most abundant type of animal in the fossil sites of the COH, often dominating the assemblages. Their keratin-sheathed horns are always diagnostic criteria by which fossil bovids can be identified. Bovids are particularly important when studying the caves in the COH. They are useful for biostratigraphic comparisons when assessing the age of fossil caves, and provide a great deal of insight into the palaeoenvironment in which hominins lived. They can also shed light on the taphonomic history of the deposits, answering questions on how the fossils came to end up in the caves, and what types of carnivores may have fed on them.

Extinct giant wildebeest

Extinct giant wildebeest *Megalotragus priscus*

The giant wildebeest *Megalotragus* was possessed of enormous, sweeping horns, fragments of which are readily recognizable. Their body weight has been estimated at 534 kg, so they were larger than modern blue wildebeest, but not as massive as a bull eland. *Megalotragus* fossils are found throughout South Africa and East Africa, indicating that this animal had a wide distribution in the Plio-Pleistocene.

The giant wildebeest probably occupied open grasslands. They also had very high-crowned teeth, an adaptation seen in all grassland grazers, but not in browsers.

Megalotragus is found in Sterkfontein Member 4, Swartkrans Members 1–3, Kromdraai A, Gladysvale, Drimolen and Coopers. In South Africa this species ranged from about 3 mya until approximately 12 000–10 000 years ago, when it became extinct.

Extinct blesbok

Extinct blesbok *Damaliscus niro*

Damaliscus niro was very similar to the modern blesbok except that it was larger and had slightly different horns. Its body weight was approximately 120 kg. Like the modern blesbok, *Damaliscus niro* was almost certainly an open grassland grazer, with a diet consisting almost exclusively of grass. It had high-crowned teeth and deep mandibles, and its skeleton was adapted for moving on relatively flat, open ground.

Damaliscus niro is found at Sterkfontein Member 5, Swartkrans Member 2 and possibly Gladysvale. *Damaliscus niro* ranged in time from about 2 mya until relatively recently, perhaps about 12 000 years ago, when it went extinct.

Extinct ovibovine *Makapania broomi*

This large, extinct bovid is remarkable in that its horns were positioned laterally. It has been referred to as an ovibovine, making its closest living relatives the musk-ox of North America and the takin of Tibet. Its body weight is estimated to have been about 263 kg.

Makapania is thought to have been both a browser and a grazer. It probably preferred grasses, and would have required a nearby source of permanent water.

Makapania broomi has been found at Sterkfontein Members 4 and 5, Swartkrans Members 1–3, Gladysvale, Motsetse and possibly Coopers. It has been recovered from 3-million-year-old sediments in East Africa. The type specimen was found at Makapansgat. This species existed from about 3 mya until 1 mya, or perhaps more recently.

Extinct ovibovine

Extinct springbok *Antidorcas bondi*

The extinct springbok, *Antidorcas bondi*, was somewhat smaller than the modern springbok, weighing on average about 25 kg. *Antidorcas bondi* was hyper-hypsodont, meaning that it had extremely high-crowned teeth. Its teeth were so high-crowned that the lower edge of its mandible was seriously distorted to fit the teeth. Such teeth are typically found in dedicated grazers, as they resist attrition to a greater extent than low-crowned teeth.

Isotopic evidence also suggests that the diet of *Antidorcas bondi* was that of an exclusive grazer. It is possible that this small springbok followed larger antelope as they grazed, feeding on the new growth that sprouted up after the larger herbivores had moved through an area.

Antidorcas bondi has been recovered from Sterkfontein Member 4, Swartkrans Members 1–3, Kromdraai A and B, Gladysvale, Motsetse, Coopers and possibly Drimolen. This species therefore existed in South Africa from 2,5 mya until about 36 000 years ago, when it finally became extinct.

Extinct giant buffalo

Extinct giant buffalo
Pelorovis antiquus

The giant buffalo was considerably larger than modern buffalo, with enormous horns stretching to as much as 3 m from tip to tip. Their body size may have exceeded 1 000 kg. The genus *Pelorovis* was found throughout East Africa and South Africa, though distinct species are known in the respective areas. The large size of the horns would have made movement in closed environments difficult, so it is probable that the giant buffalo preferred more open areas. Their extremely high-crowned teeth signify that their diet was rich in grasses. Like modern buffalo, they were probably dedicated grazers, and dependent on water.

Giant buffalo fossils are found in Swartkrans Members 1 and 2, as well as Gladysvale. They first appeared in South Africa at Swartkrans about 1,5 mya, and survived until about 10 000 years ago, when they went extinct.

Extinct reedbuck *Redunca darti*

The extinct reedbuck was slightly larger than the modern mountain reedbuck, weighing approximately 53 kg. The horns of this species were positioned more uprightly than those of its modern counterpart. The species was endemic to South Africa. The diet of *Redunca darti* probably comprised fresh grasses and was similar to, though not as specialized as, that of modern reedbuck. It was probably also quite dependent on water.

Redunca darti is known only from Gladysvale in the COH, although it has been tentatively identified at Coopers. It ranges in time from 3–2 mya, and perhaps younger.

Large rodents

Extinct porcupine *Hystrix makapanensis*

The extinct porcupine was about a third larger than modern porcupines, weighing about 16 kg. *Hystrix makapanensis* probably had a vegetarian diet, similar to that of modern porcupines, though they may have eaten more grasses. They probably had a wide habitat tolerance.

Hystrix makapanensis has been found in Swartkrans Member 1 and Kromdraai A. The species existed from 3 mya until at least 1,5 mya, if not until more recently.

GLOSSARY

A

ape-man a general term used to refer to the australopithecines, a hominin that is more 'ape' than 'human'. The term 'man-ape' is sometimes used to describe the ape-men who were beginning to display more advanced features associated with our genus, *Homo*.

arboreal adapted to living in trees.

archaeology the study of the past by scientific analysis of the material remains of human culture.

archaic something ancient, belonging to a much earlier era. Frequently used in association with more primitive forms of our own species, *Homo sapiens*

aridification the process of becoming drier. Generally refers to climatic periods during which the environment became drier and deserts formed.

artefact something made by humans. Both a stone tool and a painting are artefacts.

assemblages a number of material remains gathered together. In archaeology an assemblage refers to a grouping of tools or fossils.

Australopithecus a genus of hominin that first appeared about 4 mya and went extinct about 1 mya. Often split into two forms: robust and gracile. The gracile form was characterized by finer facial features, while the robust form can be recognized by its enormous jaws and teeth.

B

bipedalism the ability to walk on two legs. All hominins are bipedal.

bovid a member of the family Bovidae. Ruminants such as antelope are bovids.

breccia the consolidated matrix that fills a cave. It consists of sediments, rock fragments, and often bone, which are cemented together with lime to form a concrete-like rock.

C

calcium carbonate (CaCO3) a general term for lime. Lime precipitates from dolomite.

COH Cradle of Humankind

cranial capacity the volume of the brain cavity.

D

DNA deoxyribonucleic acid, the main constituent of a chromosome. DNA is responsible for the transmission of hereditary characteristics. Mitochondrial DNA is passed through the female line only and is the most common form of DNA used to calculate the date of origin of modern humans.

dolomite an ancient rock that is formed in shallow seas, consisting of lime, magnesium, and other trace minerals. Common in the Cradle of Humankind and the bedrock in which the caves form.

E

evolution the process of biological change in nature.

F

fossil a representation of a plant or animal that existed in the past. In order for an organism to become a fossil, the process of mineralization must have occurred.

G

genus a taxonomic group that divides a family and contains one or more species.

H

Holocene a time period dating from around 10 000 years ago to the present.

hominids bipedal apes that are found in the family tree of humankind. Scientists today generally refer to the hominids as 'hominins'.

hominoids a taxonomic group encompassing African apes and humans.

I

in situ in place

Iron Age In Africa, the Iron Age dates from about 2 000 years ago to the late 18th century. It was an era characterized by the use of metal for weapons and tools, and in southern Africa it is associated with the arrival of migrant pastoralists from central Africa.

M

Magaliesberg the range of mountains to the north and northwest of the Cradle of Humankind, named after Po chief Mogale.

member a geological term used to distinguish different levels or strata in cave infills. There are five main members at Sterkfontein.

microlith a small, retouched tool.

Miocene a time period lasting from about 25 mya to about 5 mya.

morphology the form or structure of an organism or its parts.

mya million years ago.

O

Oldowan the earliest commonly recognized tool industry, dating from around 2,6 mya to about 1,7 mya.

osteodontokeratic culture the bone (osteo), tooth (donto) and horn (keratic) culture, so designated by Raymond Dart to express what he believed to be the earliest culture adopted by hominins. Later discarded as having no archaeological basis.

P

palaeoanthropology the study of ancient humans and their culture.

palaeontology the study of ancient life forms.

paranthropines a general term referring to all the so-called robust australopithecines that are members of the genus *Paranthropus*.

Pleistocene a time period dating from around 1,6 mya to about 10 000 years ago.

Pliocene a time period dating from around 5 mya to about 1,6 mya.

Plio-Pleistocene the temporal period from approximately 2,5 to 1 mya. A period of transition between the Pliocene and the Pleistocene.

postcranial the bones or parts of the body from the neck down. Literally 'below the head'.

precipitation the point at which a dissolved substance, for example, lime, separates from a solution, for example water.

prognathic to jut out. In hominins, it means that the face juts forward, as in apes.

S

sediments sand or soil, usually deposited by water to form a rock layer.

sexual dimorphism the size and shape difference between males and females of the same species.

speciation the process of changing from one species to another.

species any of the taxonomic groupings into which a genus is divided. Members of a species will only breed with other members of that species.

stromatolite the fossilized remains of an ancient blue-green algae colony. Living colonies still exist in some places today.

T

taphonomy the study of the grave. The science of the reconstruction of the history of fossils and other bones from the time of an organism's death to the time of its discovery.

terrestrial living or moving on the ground.

BIBLIOGRAPHY

Berger, LR & Hilton-Barber, B. 2000. *In the Footsteps of Eve*. Washington DC: National Geographic Adventure Press.

Brain, CK. (i) 1981. *The Hunters or the Hunted?* Chicago: University of Chicago Press.

Brain, CK. (ii) 1998. 'The Swartkrans Cave Site'. In *Dual Congress Guide Book*.

Broom, R & Schepers, GWH. 1946. *The South African Fossil Ape-Men, the Australopithicinae*. Pretoria: Transvaal Museum.

Carruthers, VC. 2000. *The Magaliesberg*. Pretoria: Protea Book House.

Clarke, R. 1998. First Ever Discovery of a Well-Preserved Skull and Associated Skeleton of *Australopithecus*. In SA *Journal of Science*, vol. 94 (October).

Gregory, WK. 1939. 'The South African fossil man-apes and the origin of the human dentition'. In *Journal of the American Dental Association*, vol. 26.

Mason, R. 1962. *Prehistory of the Transvaal*. Johannesburg: Witwatersrand University Press.

SABC (South African Broadcasting Corporation). No date given. *Beyond Antiquity*. A series of radio lectures on the origin of man, arranged by Raymond Dart.

Terry, R. 1974. *Taung Anniversary Booklet*. Johannesburg: Witwatersrand University Press.

Tobias, P. 1994. 'Ad Hominidae: The Future of South Africa's Ancient Past'. In *Optima*, vol. 40, no. 1 (April).

INDEX